Hert

POTATO MECHANISATION AND STORAGE

POTATO MECHANISATION AND STORAGE

C. F. H. BISHOP, BA(Oxon)

W. F. MAUNDER, NDA, NDAgrE, MRAC, MIAgrE

FARMING PRESS LIMITED

WHARFEDALE ROAD, IPSWICH, SUFFOLK

First published 1980

ISBN 0 85236 109 2

*Set in ten on eleven point Times and printed in Great Britain on Longbow Cartridge
paper by Page Bros (Norwich) Ltd for Farming Press Limited.*

CONTENTS

APPENDICES 245

INDEX 252

ILLUSTRATIONS

TABLES

FOREWORD

OVER a period of years now I have been privileged as a farmer to have been advised by Bill Maunder, who has helped me with several projects related to potatoes and onions. He arrived in the Fens a few years ago and the experience gained whilst working in the heart of 'Potato Country' has given him a thorough knowledge of the latest techniques of Potato Mechanisation, much of which he has set down in this book.

Unfortunately he has moved away from us, but he leaves behind many successful potato growers who have benefited immensely from his advice and ideas.

I have not known Chris Bishop for quite so long but it soon became apparent to me that he had extensive knowledge of potato storage; this was borne out by the sound advice given to our growers' co-operative during the building of a large environmentally controlled potato and onion store.

We as farmers cannot speak too highly of the help we receive from all sections of the ADAS from whose ranks the authors have emerged. In the present-day climate of government cash limits and reduced manpower it is our greatest hope that the work and staff of ADAS, in whom we have such confidence, will remain unscathed to continue the valuable work that they do for farming.

Their success has already shown itself in many different ways including the ever-increasing yields from the potato crop and the dramatic improvement in the samples that are now being offered to the public.

My thanks go to Chris and Bill for setting in print the many different ways of tackling the problems of potato growing. Their clear, precise and factual writing will be of great benefit, not only to those who seek to enter the potato industry, but to those already involved who will certainly find new ideas in this book.

Doddington, November 1980.   C. D. BOUGHTON

INTRODUCTION

The last two decades have seen dramatic changes in the mechanisation and storage of the potato crop. This book deals with some of the up-to-date machinery and methods used in growing, storing and preparing potatoes for market. For reasons of space, the book does not deal with the agronomic aspects of potato production.

In writing this book, we have freely drawn on the experience gained in working as Mechanisation Advisory Officers in the Agricultural Development and Advisory Service. We are grateful to the Ministry of Agriculture, Fisheries and Food for permission to draw on results of experiments carried out by ADAS. We also thank various members of the Agricultural Research Council for use of experimental results.

Colleagues, farmers and members of the agricultural engineering industry have all willingly given assistance and we would particularly like to thank Brian Finney and David Bartlett of ADAS for their comments.

We would like to thank our two typists, Jean Eyers, and Melanie Grosse, and finally, two long-suffering wives, Stephanie and Jenny.

C. F. H. BISHOP
W. F. MAUNDER

Chapter 1

POTATO SPROUTING

INTRODUCTION

THE AIM of any potato grower is to obtain as high a profit as possible. Normally this will involve producing a large yield of quality potatoes. Obviously any method of increasing yield has to be critically examined from economic and management viewpoints, and seed potato sprouting is no exception.

The intention of seed potato sprouting (which is also known by the names of chitting, presprouting and pregermination) is to produce one or more sprouts on the tuber which are not knocked off when it is placed in the ground so that the plant has actually started growing at the time of planting. Seed potato sprouting is a method of influencing sprout growth by controlling the length and conditions of the sprouting period. The type of crop produced can also be influenced, because if apical dominance is achieved the seed tuber is more likely to produce a few large tubers rather than many small tubers.

The two main advantages in seed potato sprouting are as follows:

1. For early potatoes there is more rapid bulking of the crop. This is particularly true if apical dominance is achieved and there are just a few strong sprouts. For main crop there is also normally an increase in yield, particularly if planting is delayed or blight halts growth early.

2. Some systems allow an opportunity to inspect the crop and remove tubers which are seriously diseased.

Seed potato sprouting also has some disadvantages.

1. If the potatoes are roughly handled when they are planted the sprout can be knocked off giving disease an opportunity to break in and losing some of the growth advantage of the sprouting process.

2. To store sprouted seed costs more than to store unsprouted seed. There is also a higher labour requirement in putting the seed into the containers for sprouting and then into the planter rather than straight into the planter.

15

RECEPTION OF SEED ON TO THE FARM

Whether the intention is to sprout or not, it is very important to check the seed for any disease or mechanical or frosting damage. Therefore if seed is bought in, it should be examined immediately it is received. It is a good idea to look at one bag in twenty by taking 15 or so tubers out of the bag, alternating between removing them from the top and the bottom of the bags and washing five tubers for disease assessment. Also it is advisable to look out for any tell-tale wet patches on the bags showing rotten potatoes. If a few diseased potatoes are found, but it is decided to accept the consignment, destroy the diseased potatoes.

If the seed potatoes are known to have been harvested not more than two weeks previously they should be treated with a fungicide. However, when the seed is harvested it is advisable to cure the seed for two weeks by keeping it at a temperature of 13–16°C with high humidity. This curing process heals any wounds and stops the spread of gangrene and dry rot.

CONTAINERS

There are a number of different types of containers used for seed potato storage and it is important to consider container types both in store design and planting methods (the actual methods of supplying planters with seed and typical work rates are dealt with in Chapter 3).

Trays
These are the traditional and most common container for sprouted seed. The tray is made of wood or polythene and is 755 × 450 × 165 mm overall and 75 mm deep. It holds around 15 kg of seed. It is a convenient size and shape to lift by hand. Although polythene trays are a little tougher they cannot be repaired like wooden trays.

The rate at which trays are handled can be increased with a reduction in the manual work if the trays are put on pallets. There are specially made pallets for this purpose which have two-way entry and dimensions of 1,500 × 900 mm. The trays can be put four to a layer and stacked either seven or eight layers high giving a pallet load of 420 or 480 kg. The actual pallet unit can then be stacked three high in the store.

Bulk Box
The half-tonne box pallet can be used for seed potato sprouting although as only a few of the tubers are exposed to the light the

PLATE 1:1
Shelved box

PLATE 1:2
Mesh crates in store

eyes should just be opened, but not allowed to sprout. Ventilation through the box is essential for good control of temperature.

Normally, because of the difficulties of holding down the temperature of the potatoes in the centre of the box these containers are only used in refrigerated storage.

Mesh Bulk Crate

This type of storage container has external dimensions of $1,500 \times 910 \times 940$ mm and holds approximately 450 kg of seed. It has an outer frame made of angle iron and a weldmesh removable liner which separates the seed potatoes into columns. This arrangement means that the maximum number of potatoes are exposed to light and air.

The container can be handled as a pallet box and emptied by a tippler attachment on a fork lift.

If the sprouts on the tubers are allowed to become too long there can be difficulties with emptying as the sprouts and the weldmesh become intertwined.

Bags

Most seed potatoes are delivered to the farm in bags of 25 kg. If the intention is to keep the seed tubers without letting any sprouts develop the bags should be kept in a cool, dark place. There is a considerably higher chance of restraining any sprouts if the air can pass through the bag wall, as is the case with hessian or weaved plastic. If possible the sacks should not be put all together but stacked about six high on pallets separated from one another to allow air movement.

ENVIRONMENTAL REQUIREMENTS

If the intention is to stop the potatoes from growing any sprouts, after the initial curing period the potatoes should be kept in the dark at a temperature below 3°C and above 0°C.

However, if the intention is to sprout the potatoes, shoots of about 5 mm long, green and strong are considered ideal. If the temperature is too high the sprouts will grow too long and therefore be easily knocked off. If there is no light the sprout will be white and weak and again easily knocked off. The rate of sprouting varies with variety and the conditions of growth of the seed stock; for instance, once-grown Scottish earlies are very active.

The sprouting potatoes should be kept between 6°C and 8°C.

A higher temperature would mean the sprouts would grow too fast. If for any reason (such as bad planting weather) the sprouts need to be stopped the temperature should be dropped to below 3°C.

As light will not control excessive growth of sprouts and only a small amount is required for greening, artificial light is not required all the time in an insulated store, although of course in a glasshouse there is a high intensity of light. The subject of how much light is required is discussed under Lighting (page 24).

Humidity is rarely a problem providing that there is some ventilation in the store. If there is very high humidity the potatoes can sometimes produce masses of small roots and a fungus called Rhizoctoria can kill off the sprout tips.

Ideally at the time of planting the seed potatoes should be at the same temperature as the soil but this is rarely possible without a refrigerated store.

VENTILATION

There are considerably more problems in seed potato stores in keeping the temperature down than in keeping the temperature up. Ventilation is a very crucial part of seed potato store management in achieving even temperatures. All types of potato sprouting store require ventilation for temperature control.

In many stores ventilation is provided by opening doors and giving a through draught. This may work satisfactorily in some cases but with larger stores and ones remote from the farmhouse some form of automatic control with a fan is needed.

The fan should be capable of giving 0.05 m³/s at a pressure of 5 mm water gauge per tonne of seed (see below for details of fan performance). To achieve the best results the fan should be automatically controlled so that it only blows when required.

The form of automatic control used is called ambient ventilation control and requires three thermostats wired in series: the frost thermostat which is in the on position if the temperature is above 0°C, the store thermostat which is in the on position if the store is warmer than the preset temperature and the differential thermostat which compares the temperatures outside and inside and is in the on position if the temperature outside is colder by a preset figure. (This form of control is considered in more detail in Chapter 11.)

The positioning of the sensors of the thermostats must be considered carefully; the frost thermostat sensor should be placed just

PLATE 1:3
Propeller fan and cowl

Venduct Ltd.

upstream of the fan and out of the sun's direct rays, the store and differential thermostat sensors should be placed at approximately two-thirds of the stack height and not close to a light.

Fans

When quoting the performance of a fan it is important to give the volume it transmits and the pressure against which it is working. Without both facts any performance figure is meaningless; it would be like giving a car speed as a distance without any mention of time!

The volume a fan gives is measured in cubic metres per second and the pressure is given in millimetres of water. A pressure of 10 mm of water means that the air is capable of holding up a column of water 10 mm high.

Only two types of fans need be considered for ventilation of seed potato stores.

The first type of fan to consider is the propeller fan which has four blades, looks like a ship's propeller and is used to move large volumes of air against low pressures. It is the most common fan in seed potato stores and can be used for extracting air and moving the air around the building.

The second type of fan is the axial fan which normally has more than four blades, each of which is of aerofoil section. It is used to transmit air against slightly higher pressures (5 mm+) than the propeller fan (such as in ducting systems).

Air Distribution

Most ventilation systems for seed potato stores use pressurised systems. That is, the air is pushed into the building, rather than sucked out. The main advantage of pressurised systems is that a distribution duct can be used to ensure that the ventilating air reaches the whole building. Obviously the larger the building, the more important a duct is as air distribution becomes more crucial.

The normal design of duct is of a polythene tube which is tapered so as to ensure even air distribution. Figure 1.1 shows an example of a polythene tapered duct.

A sheet of 500 gauge polythene is used with a width equal to the circumference of the fan aperture. Therefore the width of the polythene is $\pi(D+5)$ where D is the fan diameter. The sheet is folded over and stapled between the point where the two sides meet at one end and the half-way point at the other. The area of holes required is approximately 1·7 times the cross-sectional area of the fan. The holes themselves should be 'D'-shaped with the polythene left on the vertical side of the 'D'. The flap should be left pointing outwards to ensure that the air leaves the duct at right angles.

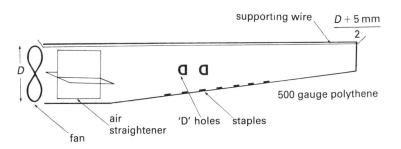

1.1 Polythene tapered duct

The duct can either be hung on strings through the surplus polythene or with a wire running right through the duct from end to end.

Although a duct is recommended, a number of stores just use a fan with high-level discharge. This can give a good temperature distribution, but careful siting of units is essential.

AIR REMOVAL

As well as entering the seed potato store air has also to come out, normally either through the natural cracks in the building or through a louvred vent. However, if air can easily escape from a building, normally it can also leak in which is undesirable as this may make the building either colder or warmer than required. Therefore the building should be well sealed and pressure-operated vents should be used. These are normally made of light-weight plastic or aluminium flaps which are lifted up by pressure from the inside but kept firmly down when a wind blows on them.

Mixing and Recirculation

The most difficult period to keep the seed potatoes cool is just before planting as ambient temperatures tend to be higher in March/April than earlier and sometimes the only cold air available is during frosty nights when it is not possible to ventilate because it is too cold. A way round this difficulty is to use what is called a Mixer Box. This consists of a box with a flap on it which mixes the air from inside the store with that from outside. This job can only be done properly by an automatic control system. The position of the flap is controlled by a thermostat downstream.

In Fig. 1.2(a) the store is ventilated entirely with fresh air but in Fig. 1.2(b) the air from outside is too cold by itself so the flap is actuated by an electronic thermostat and will move slowly across until the air stream reaches the desired temperature. (This temperature is normally set on the thermostat at 1·5°C below the temperature required in the store.

Although the average temperature may be satisfactory in a seed potato store there can be localised hot spots, particularly at high level, and it can be useful to be able to stir up the air without bringing in more from outside which might be too warm or too cold. This recirculation of air can be done in one of two ways.

The first way is to have one or more fans in the store which are used to stir up the air. Normally the fans are either the slow-moving ceiling-mounted propeller fans which are seen in offices,

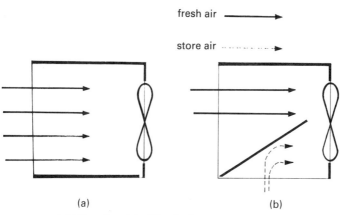

fresh air ⟶

store air ⋯⋯⋯⋯⋯▸

(a)   (b)

1.2 Mixer box (a) all fresh air
(b) mixture of store and fresh air

particularly in hot countries, or the desk-top rotating-head type of fan which can be fixed to the wall of the seed potato store. These types of fans can either be switched on manually as required or put on a timer for intermittent operation. This might be, for example, five minutes in every hour.

The second method is to use the same fan as for ventilation but to have the facility to isolate it from the outside air; it is then used for full internal recirculation. With a mixer box this can be done very easily either automatically so that once every hour the flap blocks off the outside vent and the fan comes on for five minutes or the store manager can manually change the flap when he considers it necessary.

Regular recirculation is important to achieve even temperature.

INSULATION

However good the control is over the ventilation it is virtually impossible to hold the correct temperature in a seed potato store if the building is poorly insulated.

The subject of insulation is very important when dealing with buildings for potatoes and is dealt with in detail in Chapter 12.

The standard method of expressing the insulation of a wall, roof or floor is by giving its 'U' value or thermal transmittance value measured in heat flow per unit area per degree temperature difference across the wall, roof or floor. This is given in Watts per square metre per degree Centigrade ($W/m^2{}^{\circ}C$).

In the case of a refrigerated store the 'U' value should be below 0·5 W/m²°C and preferably below 0·4 W/m²°C. If the insulation is not of this standard the refrigeration equipment will be running much of the time, giving very high running costs and dehydration.

In the case of an insulated building with artificial lights the 'U' value should be below 0·75 W/m²°C. The better the insulation the more the store is capable of withstanding temperature fluctuations outside.

It is not possible to insulate a glasshouse (unless by double glazing) so it is much more liable to temperature fluctuations particularly between day and night. This is one of the principal drawbacks in the use of glasshouses.

LIGHTING

In the case of an insulated ambient ventilated building or a refrigerated store (except for mini sprouting) artificial lights are needed. As mentioned earlier the reason for the lights is to ensure that the sprouts produced are green and strong.

The number of lights required varies with different management requirements and different varieties. As a rule of thumb the amount of light required is 65 W/tonne for maincrop and 85 W/tonne for earlies.

The fluorescent tube lights used are 'warm white' as these produce a lower amount of heat for a given light intensity than other types of tube lights. These lights come in a number of sizes such as in Table 1.1.

TABLE 1.1

	Approx cost £
2·0m 85W	30
2·5m 85W	33
2·5m 125W	35
2·5m 80W (2 × 40W)	38
3·0m 160W (2 × 80W)	42
3·5m 170W (2 × 85W)	45
4·0m 210W (1 × 125W + 1 × 85W)	50

The lights can be arranged so that they hook on to the side of the container; otherwise they are suspended from the ceiling on a rail, or they can be provided with a base and be free standing and placed in the passages between containers which are typically 0·5 m wide.

In most cases the lights are turned on for around 8–10 hours which is gradually increased to 12–14 hours just before the intended time for planting. These hours of light are normally at night when the grower can take the opportunity of cheap-rate electricity and the outside conditions are cooler.

Normally for maincrop potatoes the lights are moved on a tray length (or 0·75 m) daily for four days and then back again. For earlies the sequence takes three days as opposed to four.

If possible the inside of the store should be painted white in order to make maximum use of reflected light.

CURING

As mentioned before under 'Reception of Seed on to the Farm' (page 16) all seed should be cured when it first arrives. The potatoes should be kept at 13–16°C with high humidity for two weeks so that any wounds can be healed and any gangrene or dry rot halted.

The problems of curing arise when the seed potatoes for one store do not all arrive on the farm together so some potatoes are fully cured before others arrive. There are only two ways of solving this problem and neither of them is really satisfactory.

The first method of dealing with staggered curing is to have a separate insulated building which is used to cure the potatoes which are then moved to the cooler environment of the potato sprouting store. The difficulties of this system are that the potatoes have to be double handled and extra capital cost is incurred in the provision of a separate curing house.

The second method is to have an insulated partition which can separate off part of the potato sprouting store. This can work well but has two problems. Firstly, unless the partition is moveable the proportion of cured to uncured potatoes is unlikely to be correct, particularly if the seed potatoes arrive in three or more batches. Secondly, the ventilation system has to be able to operate for only part of the store as clearly the cured potatoes cannot be left unventilated for two weeks. One possible type of moveable partition is an insulated quilt which can work well provided care is taken to ensure that it rests on the ground and is not torn.

TYPES OF POTATO SPROUTING STORE

Basically there are three main types of potato sprouting store: glasshouses, insulated light-proof stores and refrigerated stores.

PLATE 1:4
Glasshouse potato sprouting store

Glasshouse

A glasshouse is the cheapest new building that can be erected for potato sprouting. The actual running costs can be low but there are normally high maintenance costs as a glasshouse is susceptible to damage, in particular from high winds, but also from any careless driving of a tractor or fork lift. Damage is obviously particularly serious if it occurs when the potatoes are in store.

The more modern glasshouses allow easy access and pallet handling of trays. As there is a lack of temperature control, trays are the best containers to use. They have the advantages of ease of inspection and management. Allow 150 mm between pallets in each row so that more of the potatoes receive some light. Half a metre is a suitable distance to be left between rows to walk down.

As natural light is the sole light source there can be somewhat irregular greening particularly between the trays on the top and the trays in the centre at the bottom. Some growers actually move the trays around but this is a very labour-intensive task and of doubtful value. The normal method of ventilation is to open the doors at each end of the glasshouse. One case is known where the glasshouse is ventilated by two fans with a thermostat and this gives less of a temperature variation than the normal glasshouse.

Temperature control in a glasshouse is limited by season and location, although the large quantities of light often make up for this deficiency and help produce tough green sprouts. One common problem is when too many containers are put in the glasshouse resulting in excessive shading of some trays.

Obviously a glasshouse is poorly insulated so heat is required for frost protection. Normally a 3 kW heater for every 10 tonne of potatoes is adequate.

As an example of temperature control Table 1.2 shows a record that was kept in spring 1978 of a modern 120 tonne aluminium glasshouse (dimensions 7·6 × 27·5 m, eaves height 4 m).

TABLE 1.2

	Glasshouse temperature	Ambient temperature
Percentage of time above 7·5°C	52·2%	18·4%
Percentage of time between 2·5° and 7·5°C	47·8%	39·2%
Percentage of time below 2·5°C	0%	42·4%

(period of temperature record 16 January–19 March)

Cost
The typical cost in May 1980 for a 100 tonne store before grant would be approximately £14,600.

Example 1.1
Consider a grower who wishes to sprout 100 tonne of potatoes and decides to put up a glasshouse.

Trays would be used, three to 50 kg: therefore 6,000 trays.

Assuming palletised system used, each pallet eight trays high, four per layer (0·9 × 1· ×1·35 m high).

$$\text{Therefore 188 pallets needed.} \left(\frac{6000}{8 \times 4} = 187{\cdot}5 \right)$$

If the pallets are stacked two high in lines 0·5 m apart with 150 mm between each one, various combinations of glasshouse dimensions can be calculated:

```
3 rows wide...  4·2 m × 52·8 m
6 rows wide...  8·9 m × 26·4 m
9 rows wide...12·6 m × 18·2 m.
```

From this and the available sizes of glasshouses the dimensions of 9·0 m × 27·0 m are selected.

Allowing a 3 kW heater per 10 tonne, electric sockets for 10 3 kW heaters should be installed.

A door large enough for a tractor and trailer (3·6 m square) should be incorporated at each end to allow easy handling.

PLATE 1:5
Eight-foot long fluorescent tube lighting

Insulated Store with Lights
Providing there is ample insulation and ventilation with good control, this type of store can generally, within the limits imposed by outside air conditions, provide the desired temperatures. This last factor is particularly relevant to planting where it is not always possible to cool the crop to soil temperature.

Artificial lights are used to induce greening and toughening of sprouts and it must be remembered that lights do produce heat so it is essential to be able to remove this heat. Typical light requirement is 65 W/tonne.

Ventilation should be provided by a fan at the rate of 0·05 m³/s per tonne of seed.

As stated previously the insulation should be such that the thermal transmittance (the 'U' value) is below 0·75 W/m²°C.

This type of building is suitable for the use of either trays or cellular mesh containers if there is ambient ventilation control.

Heating is very rarely needed except during the curing period and most potato growers install a few extra electric sockets so that, if required, electric heaters can be put in the store. As a rule of thumb the facility for one 3 kW heater for every 25 tonne should be put in. It must be remembered that both the lights and the potatoes themselves produce heat.

Most modern stores have doors large enough to allow easy access and pallet handling. If possible, doors should be positioned at both ends so that the seed potatoes can be removed in the opposite order to which they were put in.

As an example of temperature control Table 1.3 shows a record that was kept in spring 1978 of a 100–120 tonne modern lightproof insulated building with ambient air ventilation (including a mixer box) and lights. (dimensions 24·4 m × 12·2 m, 4·6 m to eaves).

TABLE 1.3

	Store temperature	Ambient temperature
Pecentage of time above 7·5°C	15·3%	18·4%
Percentage of time between 2·5°C and 7·5°C	83·9%	39·2%
Percentage of time below 2·5°C	0·8%	42·4%

(period of temperature record 16 January–19 March)

The heater was set to come on at 1·5°C and this occurred once.

Cost
The typical cost in May 1980 for a 100 tonne store before grant would be approximately £22,000.

Example 1.2
Consider a grower who wishes to sprout 100 tonne of potatoes and decides to put up an insulated building with lights.

Using a palletised tray system (6,000 trays are needed as three trays take 50 kg of seed) with eight layers of four trays on each pallet (0·9 × 1·5, 1·35 m high).

$$\text{Therefore 188 pallets needed} \left(\frac{6000}{8 \times 4} = 187 \cdot 5 \right)$$

To fit in with the other farm buildings the decision is to go for a building 13·5 m wide.

One possible system is shown in Fig. 1.3 with a building 15 m long.

PLATE 1:6
Insulated store

As a palletised system has been considered, it is important to remember the turning circle of the fork lift, therefore normally the end of the building is stacked as indicated in Fig. 1.3. Obviously if room is very tight, the last few trays are stacked by hand.

The height of the pallets is 4·05 m (1·35 × 3) so an eaves height of around 4·2 m is suggested and roof pitch of 22°.

The building should be insulated to a 'U' value of less than 0·75 W/m^2°C such as 50 mm of glass fibre and double skin asbestos. Doors (approx 3·6 m square) should be put at each end so the potatoes do not have to be taken out in the opposite order to which they were put in.

Allowing a 3 kW heater per 25 tonne, electric sockets for four 3 kW heaters should be installed. Working on the design guide of 65 W/tonne for lighting and with the lights put as shown on the diagram twenty-four lights will be needed. Assuming they are 4 m 210 W lights they actually give 50·4 W/tonne which is acceptably close to the intended figure.

door

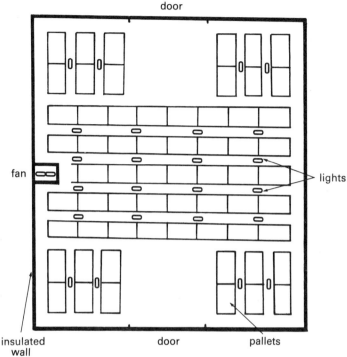

fan   lights

insulated   door   pallets
wall

1.3 Layout of pallets for Example 1.2

For ventilation a fan capable of $5\,m^3/s$ at 5 mm w.g. with distribution duct should be installed. The best place for this is half way up one side. For optimum control there should be a mixer box with ambient ventilation control as mentioned previously.

If the same example had been considered with cellular bulk crates instead of palletised trays the same building would have been used but the crates could have been stacked four high giving a height of $3\cdot76\,m$ ($4 \times 0\cdot94$). With each crate taking an average of 450 kg the same building with the same stacking configuration would take around 107 tonne.

Refrigerated Store with Lights
This system allows total control over both temperature and lighting and therefore there is flexibility over the choice of containers. As there is the facility for cooling the temperature can be reduced to the soil temperature just prior to planting. This allows the potato blueprint to be followed.

Artificial lights are used to induce greening and toughening of the sprouts. As the lights produce heat, the installation of a thermostat as well as the normal time switch is suggested. If, with the refrigeration plant running, the temperature continued to rise as a result of excessively high outside temperatures the lights would then be switched off. Typical light requirement is 65 W/tonne.

An air circulation fan capable of 40 circulations of the empty store volume per hour should be used to ensure even temperatures throughout the store.

It is very important that the temperature difference (T.D.) across the coils of the refrigeration plant is not too large or the relative humidity will be too low resulting in drying out of the potatoes. Something in the order of 6°C or less is suggested.

The initial cost of a refrigerated store is high as is the running cost although there is a limited application for alternative uses such as short-term storage of vegetables in the summer season.

The doors to the store should have a good seal and there should be a separate personnel door so that the store can be inspected without opening the main doors.

As stated previously the insulation should be such that the thermal transmittance (the 'U' value) is below 0·5 W/m^2°C.

It is highly unlikely that heating will be needed except during the curing period when a space heater can be used. However it is probably worth putting in one electric socket for a 3 kW heater for every 30 tonne.

The temperature control is very good with this type of store and as an example a temperature record was kept in the spring of 1978 in one store and the temperature varied between 3·5°C and 5·5°C during the whole time (16 January–19 March).

Cost

The typical cost in May 1980 for a 100 tonne store before grant would be approximately £30,000.

Example 1.3

Consider a grower who wishes to sprout 100 tonne of potatoes in a refrigerated store.

The same dimensions of building and layout of potatoes would be used as in Example 1.2 with a few differences; only one large door would be used rather than two as there are problems of air leaking in; a separate personnel door would be included, and the insulation would be improved so that the 'U' value was below 0·5 W/m^2°C. About 50 mm of spray-on foam plastic on asbestos would be suitable.

The main difference is that refrigeration equipment is used and the cooling load is estimated as follows.

The largest refrigeration load will occur in the spring when there can be warm weather and also the lights are required to be on, as shown in Table 1.4.

TABLE 1.4 Maximum refrigeration load

Leakage (structure)	1·878 kW
(air)	0·674 kW
Fan	2·600 kW
Lights	5·725 kW
Respiration	1·000 kW
Total load	11·877 kW

It is standard practice to include a design margin in the refrigeration sizing calculations but in this case as the lights are such a large proportion of the total load they should be on a thermostat. Then if the refrigeration equipment cannot keep the temperature down the lights go off.

The following assumptions have been made in calculating the maximum refrigeration load.

(a) The 'U' value is $0.5 \text{ W/m}^2{}^{\circ}\text{C}$ on both walls and ceiling.
(b) The intended temperature in the store is 6°C and the outside temperature is 15°C.
(c) The fan required to recirculate the air has a capacity of 40 times the room's empty volume per hour $(40 \times 830 \text{ m}^3)$.
(d) An additional 19 W per light has been included for control gear.
(e) The respiration rate for the potatoes has been taken as 10W/tonne.
(f) The air infiltration rate is 0·25 empty volumes/hour.

It is highly unlikely that heaters will ever be required but four electric sockets for 3 kW electric heaters could be included.

MINI SPROUTING

One of the difficulties with potato sprouting is the danger of the sprouts being knocked off in planting. Mini sprouting (or mini-chitting) is an attempt to have some of the advantages of normal sprouting but not the risks at planting. This is done by just opening the eyes of the tuber and having sprouts one or two millimetres long.

The method of doing this is to allow the eyes to open during the curing period and then quickly bring down the temperatures to 3°C or below to restrict any further growth. About two weeks before planting the temperature should be raised to 6–7°C. As no lights are needed bulk containers can be used.

The big problem with mini sprouting is that it is crucial to be able to hold the temperature down when required. If the temperature rises the tubers will sprout and as there is no light the sprouts will be white and weak.

As there is this problem with holding temperatures, refrigeration is really needed which means that mini sprouting requires a high capital cost. However, as no lights are needed, the containers can be stacked together with no passages, so the volume of building required per tonne is substantially reduced. Normally the yield advantage over unsprouted potatoes obtained with mini sprouting would not be quite as high as with standard sprouting methods.

NEW DEVELOPMENTS

The methods of seed potato sprouting be it storage, handling or containers are developing all the time and one recent development is the transparent plastic house.

With the recent developments in plastics it is now possible to have large lightweight sheets of transparent plastic. A number of portal framed buildings with heights of 4·5 m or more to the eaves have been built with transparent plastic cladding. This gives the advantage of ample light like a glasshouse without the high labour cost of glazing. With ambient ventilation control these can give quite satisfactory control of temperature. Although it is too early to know what sort of lifespan these buildings will have, the plastic sheets have not gone quickly opaque.

SUMMARY

● Containers for sprouting
● Tray, bulk box, shelved box, cellular bulk crate
● Temperatures involved:

Curing   13–16°C   for two weeks
Sprouting   6–8°C
Holding   3–4°C

(These are typical temperatures but they will differ with variety.)
● Requirements for sprouting stores are shown in Table 1.5

PLATE 1:7
Seed potato store with large lightweight sheets of transparent plastic

TABLE 1.5

	Ventilation per tonne	Insulation 'U' value	Heat per tonne	Light per tonne
Glasshouse	normally natural ventilation by opening doors	—	300 W	—
Insulated store with lights	0·05 m³/s	0·75 W/m²°C	120 W	65 W
Refrigerated store with lights	40 air volumes/hr for the whole store	0·5 W/m²°C	100 W	65 W

References

THE ELECTRICITY COUNCIL, *Electricity and Potato Husbandry*, 1969.
MAUNDER W. F. AND BISHOP C. F. H., 'Potato Chitting Stores: four case studies', ADAS 1978 (unpublished).
MINISTRY OF AGRICULTURE, FISHERIES AND FOOD, *Seed Potato Sprouting*, Advisory leaflet 504, Revised 1978.

Chapter 2

CULTIVATIONS FOR POTATOES

BEFORE DISCUSSING the range of cultivation equipment available for potato cultivation it is necessary to outline the requirements of the potato. The method of cultivation is vital in achieving the maximum yield of good-shaped, undamaged tubers and to achieve a ridge that can be lifted quickly with little if any hand labour. It is also important for adequate weed control.

Good drainage is essential to prevent any flooding in the ridge, to make possible early timely cultivations and to allow good harvesting conditions. Therefore subsoiling may be necessary the previous autumn. Ploughing should be finished early in the autumn, before the soil is over wet and should be level so that the frost mould is not lost between the ridges. In the spring the soil should be fine to the full depth at which the tubers grow and it should be moist. These two requirements are not always compatible, as every tilth-producing operation will allow moisture to escape. Soil moisture can be maintained by speediness during the planting cultivations. To some extent the soil tilth is determined by the choice of cultivation equipment.

CLODS

There are many agronomic reasons for keeping the soil free of clods, but the major reasons are mechanical. Clods which are similar to or of greater size than the potatoes at harvest must be separated mechanically or by pickers. In dry seasons clods can become sharp-edged causing damage to tubers. An ideal maximum soil aggregate size is no more than 12 mm.

STONES

Stones smaller than 12 mm can be an advantage in keeping the soil separate in the ridge, but above this size they begin to be a problem, being difficult to separate at harvest and causing damage to tubers. Stone and clod can be removed on suitable soils. Stone separation, removal and crushing will be discussed later in this chapter.

CULTIVATIONS

Ploughing

Potato land requires ploughing usually no deeper than 200–250 mm in early autumn, except on the lighter soil where spring ploughing is possible. Trash burying is essential; skimmers should be used to achieve this. Rotavating or discing prior to ploughing may help. One-way ploughing is an advantage producing a level surface for subsequent once-over cultivations.

The semi-digger plough which tends to produce a flatter top to the ploughing is preferred. The frost mould formed during the winter months will not be lost between the furrows.

Pre-planting Cultivations

In the final tilth there should be plenty of fine soil to a depth of 100–150 mm. On heavy soils the frost mould must be kept on the soil surface. Working the soil should not start too early or soil compaction to the soft moist soil under the surface will result. In dry conditions the land should receive its final cultivation and be planted on the same day to keep soil moisture loss to the minimum.

It is essential when considering the choice of cultivation equipment to remember that the intention is to keep the soil where it is and not to change its position. Fine frost mould must not be buried or raw moist clod brought to the surface which will subsequently dry out and produce hard damaging clod. The intention is to cut or crush clod where its lies. On difficult soil it may be necessary progressively to increase cultivation depth rather than to go to full depth in one go.

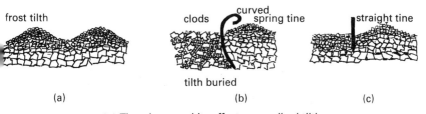

2.1 Tine shape and its effect on seedbed tilth

Influence of tine shape on final seedbed tilth:
  (a) Ploughed land in the spring;
  (b) Clods brought up by spring-tine cultivations and frost tilth buried;
  (c) Frost tilth left on surface by straight-tined harrow.

PRE-PLANTING CULTIVATORS

The straight-tine cultivator: this is normally termed a Dutch drag harrow. It has a large number of closely-spaced spiked tines on large section tine bars often made from wood. The tines can work to a depth of 150 mm and being straight tines, alternately spaced on up to five tine bars, they shatter the clod without bringing wet soil to the surface. The tool is often fitted with a heavy angled levelling board at the front with a cage roller crumbler at the rear. On suitable soils this equipment can provide a seedbed in one pass. A 3 m model would require a tractor of approximately 75 kW. Spring-tine cultivators can be used but care is essential to avoid bringing raw moist soil to the surface as this will form clod when it dries out.

Powered Implements

The powered cultivator is becoming widely used in potato pre-planting cultivations. It is important, however, that the land is not over cultivated, as too fine a tilth will tend to run together in the ridges, particularly on unstable soils.

There are a number of different types of powered cultivator available. Each has its own particular properties and choice will depend to a large extent on soil type.

Reciprocating Harrows

This implement has two or three horizontal bars with vertical harrow tines on each set of bars. The bars alternately oscillate from side to side at up to 500 cycles per minute. This cultivator has a similar effect to the drag harrow, but has a more vigorous action which will also crush some clod. Overuse of this tool could lead to some of the fine tilth being lost to the lower levels. Its action and power consumption are not as great as the rotary cultivators.

Rotary Harrows

This implement has gained in popularity as a potato cultivator in recent years. This implement consists of pairs of gear-driven rotors, contra-rotating about a vertical axis and revolving at 250–300 rpm. The powered harrow is not suitable for cultivating new ground, but like the reciprocating harrow produces a fine tilth without bringing raw soil from below during secondary cultivations. It is available in widths from 1 metre to 6 metres and requires pto power from 30 to 112 kW. A rotary cage crumbler is invariably fitted which will control depth of work, level the surface and crush surface clods.

PLATE 2:1
Rotary cultivators—Hook tine cultivator with crumbler roller

Hoekstra Trading Co. Ltd

Rotary Cultivators

There are three basic types of rotary cultivator: the conventional rotavator with 'L'-shaped blades; the spike rotavator, and the hooked-tine rotavator. All three types have a robust horizontal shaft which runs the full width of the machine. This shaft rotates usually in the same direction as the tractor wheels and is driven through a gear box from the pto of the tractor. The speed of rotation of the tines compared to ground speed can be selected by the appropriate ratio of the cultivator's gear box and choice of forward speed of the tractor. The combination of choice of forward speed and speed of shaft rotation will decide the type of tilth formed. With high-powered tractors there is a tendency to produce an over-fine tilth by travelling slowly with a high rotor speed. This is often a waste of time and power leading to increased wear on tines and implement, and often soil structure is lost.

The 'L'-shaped blade does have a basic disadvantage and that is the tendency to cause smearing at the extremity of the cultivation depth. Improved blade design has tended to minimise this, but under certain soil conditions depending on soil moisture and soil type and particularly heavy soils, smearing and the formation of a pan can occur. Slow forward speed combined with high rotor speed is more likely to lead to smearing.

The alternative tines get over this smearing problem and produce a rougher tilth. The spiked rotor is particularly good for smashing clods and has a very much reduced power requirement.

The hook tine cultivator uses self-sharpening tines which by their action tend to scratch the soil, removing small pieces—rather than cutting it with a blade. The machine has proved particularly effective, producing adequate tilths in one pass on heavy silt soils.

This cultivator can be fitted with a rear crumbler roller or ridging bodies which allow the land to be ridged before planting. Pre-ridging does have the advantage of maintaining constant row widths with high-speed planters as the tractor wheels will run in the base of the ridge.

One manufacturer of a hook-tine cultivator suggests a cultivation system for potatoes using the full width and inter-row versions of the cultivator. The level ploughing just before planting is cultivated with the full-width cultivator to a depth of 75 mm. This will normally give a tilth depth of 100–125 mm. The potatoes are then planted 25 mm above the uncultivated soil but above the furrow bottom. Only a small ridge is formed. After planting, the rotary cultivator is converted to an 'inter-row' cultivator and then ridging bodies are fitted and the crop ridged up—cultivating at a depth sufficient to provide a rough tilth to form a good ridge. Hook-tine cultivators are available with widths from 2 m to 4 m requiring a tractor of 40–75 kW when used as a full-width cultivator.

POTATO RIDGES

Ridge Size and Shape

Experimental work has shown that the ideal ridge for 750–900 mm row has a cross-sectional area of about 0·075 sq.m. This is big enough to contain a 50 tonne per hectare crop without undue greening. A ridge of this size has a 200 mm depth of mould above the uncultivated soil and a base of 550–650 mm when freshly made.

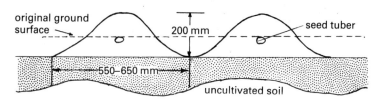

2.2 An ideal potato ridge

Row Width and Wheelings

Every new set of wheelings before planting and after ploughing will compact more tilth and is likely to make more clod. Cage wheels or dual-wheels should be used to reduce the effect of wheelings; alternatively there are two further methods that can be used to reduce the problem. The first method ensures that all passes after ploughing including fertiliser spreading and all cultivations take place in the same wheelings. In the autumn the field is accurately marked out with a tractor, and markers are used for each operation. Wheelings and compaction can be restricted to the minimum area possible and the soil under the eventual ridges left uncompacted by wheels. The other method is to protect the frost mould from wheel compaction by moving the tilth aside from the wheel track by fitting front-mounted ridging bodies on the tractor before each wheel.

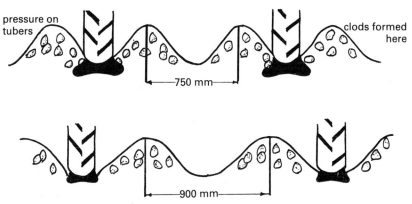

2.3 Wider rows for potatoes reduces pressure damage to tubers and clod formation at the ridge sides

Clod can also be caused at the bottom and on the sides of the ridges by tyres after the crop has been planted. This effect can be reduced by going for wider row widths; rows wider than 750 mm are an advantage, 900 mm widths are preferred. This allows the ridge to be made up from a reduced depth of tilth and also provides greater space for the wheels. This increased space reduces compaction on the edge of the ridges. Further advantages are an increased harvesting rate of up to 17 per cent and less likelihood of tubers being damaged at the sides of the ridge due to wheel pressure from tractors and harvesters.

PLATE 2:2
Three-row tined cultivator with mouldboard ridger bodies

J. W. Blench

PLATE 2:3
Rolling cultivator and ridger

Opico

Equipment for Ridging and Inter-row Cultivation

Ridging prior to planting is carried out by some growers for a number of reasons. They feel it is an aid to accurate planting when using high-speed planters. It also avoids the planter tractor travelling on the newly-formed tilth which could in some conditions lead to clod formation. But it is important that the wheelings of the planter tractor do not form a pan in the bottom of the ridge. To avoid this, it is common practice to split the ridge when planting: the tubers lying in soil unaffected by wheels. It is common practice also to use a ridger with a row number different from that of the planter, for example a three-row ridger for a two-row planter; this ensures that row spacings are even across the field.

The essential elements of ridging up and inter-row cultivation are to keep moisture loss to the minimum and not bring clod into the ridge. The range of equipment available for ridging and inter-row cultivation has been developed to meet the varying requirements of soil type and condition.

Mouldboard Ridger

This is the basic unit for ridging prior to planting and will form the ridging body of the majority of inter-row cultivators. The ridger body consists of two opposite mouldboards about a central share.

Mouldboards are often designed so that they can be adjusted for spread to decrease or increase ridge height and to suit different row spacings. Ridger design is important; the ridger shape suitable for 700 mm rows is not necessarily suitable for 900 mm rows. A broad share to reduce the angle of the mouldboard and to give a flat base to the furrow is often preferred. In wet heavy soil conditions the mould board ridger can cause smearing to the ridge sides leading to clod formation.

Inter-row Cultivation and Ridging

There are three basic types of inter-row cultivator:
   (a) Tined cultivators with ridger bodies;
   (b) Powered rotary cultivator with ridger bodies;
   (c) Rotary ridger.

Tined Cultivators with Ridger Bodies

There are various types within this grouping, but basically they consist of spring or solid tines, usually seven or eight in number mounted on a 'V' body which is adjustable for width and individual tine depth. The 'V'-shaped cultivator unit body is usually set to give a progressive cultivation action effected by increasing the tine

PLATE 2:4
Powered rotary cultivator with ridger bodies

PLATE 2:5
Close-up view of helically mounted bar tines and share of rotary ridger

Chieftain Forge Ltd

depth from front to the back of the assembly. Disc or mouldboard ridger units are fitted directly behind each of the cultivation units for moulding up the tilth formed.

The cultivator can be fitted with light rake weeder units which are positioned over each ridge to cultivate the top of the ridge lightly and control weeds.

Within this grouping comes the rolling cultivator, an example of which is the Lilliston by Opico. This implement has rotating cast-iron tines which revolve as a reaction to their contact with the soil. The tines or blades are mounted in banks which are independently adjustable for angle and inclination. Alternate gangs can be set to left and right. This angling causes soil to be moved to one side, as well as turning the soil is cut into small particles ideal for ridge forming. Careful setting of the banks and gangs of tines produces a high-speed tool for earthing up. Some growers have combined the tool with conventional ridger bodies but this should not normally be necessary.

Powered Inter-row Cultivators with Ridging Bodies
The rotary inter-row cultivators are based on the full-width hook-tine cultivators. The cultivator uses the self-sharpening hook tines which tear at the soil leaving a granular tilth and providing a pervious base to the furrow which allows drainage in wet periods. Implements are available for cultivating up to five rows, at row spacing from 700 mm to 900 mm. The implement can be readily converted from full-width to inter-row cultivator. For earthing-up conventional mouldboard ridgers mounted on parallelogram linkages for independent depth control are mounted at the rear of the machine.

The power requirement is very much less than in the full-width equivalents.

Rotary Ridgers
The SIAE rotary ridger was developed as an alternative to the mouldboard ridger by the Scottish Institute of Agricultural Engineering. The machine manufactured by Chieftain Forge Ltd uses shaped tined rotors to set up the ridge. The machine is available in three and five rotor models with the row width setting built in at the factory. However, it is possible to alter it later with little trouble if required. The range of settings is from 700 mm to 970 mm.

Each ridging unit is based on two conical hubs mounted on a chain case and on a shaft which is driven from the tractor pto through gears and chains. The bar-type tines are mounted helically on the hubs and revolve in the same direction as the forward travel, cultivating and moving the soil up and to the side to form the ridge. On the bottom of each chain case is mounted a share similar to the conventional ridger, but without the mouldboards. Tines and shares are easily renewable. Because the tines are of different lengths on the hub, as they wear they can be progressively moved along and only one or two long tines require replacement at any one time. It is claimed that this ridger can successfully work in damp and hard soil conditions and lead to a sharp reduction in the amount of clod formed in the ridge. It is also claimed to avoid the hard shoulder on the ridge often formed by conventional mouldboard ridgers.

STONE REDUCTION AND REMOVAL TREATMENTS

Stones present a problem in growing and harvesting potatoes. They can displace soil which could retain nutrients and moisture, they slow the passage of harvesters and they cause considerable damage to the very susceptible potato tubers. There are three methods of dealing with the problem:
- collecting and windrowing stones for one season;
- removing stones the previous autumn or during the spring before planting;
- reducing stone size by crushing.

Stone Windrowing

Stone windrowing machines separate the stones and clods from raised beds or ridges just before planting and then place the separated material into an adjacent furrow. The implements are similar to the potato elevator digger and comprise a digging share and separating web through which the fine soil falls and the clods and stones are transferred by cross-conveyors or chutes to form a windrow between the re-formed ridges. A good soil depth is required to provide sufficient soil for the ridge after separation. The spacing between the web bars decides the minimum size of stone separated; normally this is about 25 mm.

There are three methods of stone windrowing. The Scorgie Braemar has two shares and elevating webs, each separating two half ridges and placing the stones and clods by chutes into the furrows made by the floating ridging bodies under the body of the machine. Large heavy-duty spring tines set behind the tractor wheels loosen the soil and assist in the formation of the furrow for the stone windrows. Rate of work is about 4 ha/day when using

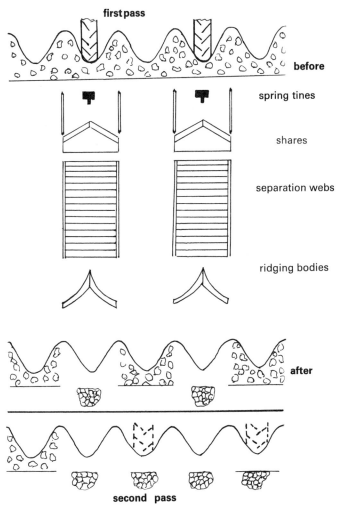

2.4 Scorgie Braemar stone and clod separating system

a 56 kW tractor. Planting normally takes place straight after windrowing—splitting the ridges formed and earthing-up after planting with a ridger body as a separate operation to avoid bringing stones into the ridge.

The Reekie stone and clod separator with a 1·25 m wide share will lift a ridge bed which is prepared by a five-row ridger at

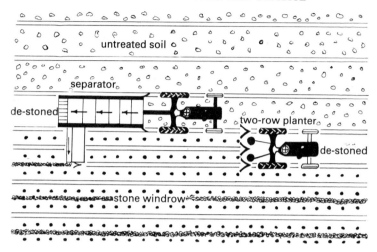

2.5 Plan view of alternate furrow stone windrowing (Reekie system)

700 mm, 750 mm or 900 mm centres with the second and the fourth bodies removed, or by a three-row ridger with the second body removed.

Above the share a spiked intake rotor and the primary web (which runs faster than the secondary separation web), combine to reduce operating draught, break up the soil and improve intake. To retain the separated soil, twin-ridge reflector plates are positioned under the web. Stones over 125 mm in diameter are collected by a hopper at the rear of the machine. A cross-conveyor transfers the smaller stones and clods over the previously planted twin ridges to form a windrow into a furrow made by an opener and stone windrowing plough.

Planting and windrowing the stones at the same time has a number of advantages. Planting and ridging can take place without the risk of taking the windrowed stones into the ridges and the soil is in an ideal condition for planting, being fine and moist. However, it does rely on both the planter and windrower working reliably. Rate of work is around 3·3 ha/day when operating at a soil depth of 230 mm and removing about 240 tonne/ha. The machine will require a tractor of at least 44 kW.

The Benedict B-W stone separator is similar in design, but with a single web with a width of 1·8 metres. The stones are windrowed directly to the side of the machine, being transferred by a cross-conveyor to a chute and windrowing plough. The wheels of the machine press the clods and stones deep into the furrow bottom.

This machine can be fitted with elevator units so that complete stone removal can be carried out, which can be useful when field stone content is excessive.

Stone Removal

As mentioned, most stone windrowers can be used to give complete stone removal, but there are specialist machines for this purposes, called stone pickers. These machines work at depths from 38 mm to 150 mm. With the shallow working machines, it would be necessary to bring the stones to the surface with cultivations. The machines use shares, heavy-duty pick-up reels or rakes to collect the stone. Separating mechanism include webs, rotary barrel drums and reciprocating riddles. The stones are either collected in a hopper or transferred to the trailer by discharge elevator.

Stone Crushing

Stone-crushing machines are designed to reduce the size of the stone so that it will pass through the harvesting webs and reduce the harvesting problems. It is possible to treat the stones and soil *in-situ*, but the most suitable method for potato land is to lift and separate the soil from the stone and then crush it within the machine.

The Ramsey stone-crushing machine has a 1·4 metre wide share with a short intake web; a secondary conveyor web with rubber flights and a 25 mm gap separates the stones and clods and transfers them to the two pairs of crushing rollers.

One roller of each pair is driven by a hydraulic motor and the other is spring-loaded to assist with the shattering effect of the rollers. Stones up to 200 mm in diameter can be crushed successfully and the machine can deal with about 3·3 hectares per day when crushing about 150 tonnes of material per hectare. Repair costs for this type of machine are likely to be higher than for windrowers because of the wear and tear of crushing.

Recently a number of combined stone windrowers and planters have been developed. On the prototype Reekie machine the planter is mounted on top of the machine with a large storage platform for seed. The seed potatoes are fed by a conveyor system to under the body of the machine to be planted directly into the separated soil. On another machine the two row planter is mounted directly behind the stone separator.

What is the most suitable stone treatment for the potato crop? Experimental work at the Ministry of Agriculture Experimental Husbandry Farm at Gleadthorpe has shown that with stone win-

PLATE 2:6
Stone and clod reduced potato ridges being produced by
three-row Scorgie 3 stone and clod separator

PLATE 2:7
Benedict stone windrower at work

PLATE 2:8
Reekie combined potato planter and stone windrower

drowing severe tuber damage has been reduced by up to 60 per cent. The amount of stone and clod on the potato harvester web after separation is similar for windrowers and stone pickers, but there is usually more clod and stone with crushers. Increased harvesting rates of up to 25 per cent can be expected after stone treatment with stone windrowing and stone removal; stone crushing has not shown such an increase, nor has the level of damage been reduced so much. The reduction in clod and stone means that unmanned harvesters can be used where manned harvesters were necessary before treatment and a reduction in labour requirement will result. In fact, there is a risk when the crusher is used on some types of stone of producing sharp particles of stone which could increase damage levels.

Stone removal and crushing can, particularly on soils of unstable structure, lead to permanent damage to the physical condition of the soil. Great care is therefore required when considering choice of system.

SUMMARY

The way in which the cultivations are carried out will affect the crop right through to storage. It can affect yield. The amount of clod and stone will decide the method and ease of harvesting, with less clod and stone leading to a reduction in tuber damage. The choice of row width will decide the extent of greening, the amount of pressure damage due to wheels and the work rate of the harvester. The ease with which harvesting can take place is dependent on the cultivations in the spring. An easy harvest can, with care, mean less tuber damage, fewer problems in store and a greater proportion of saleable ware.

Chapter 3

PLANTERS AND PLANTING

WITH NO other crop is the farmer faced with such a choice of planting methods. Planters are available in six basic types, from the simple hand-fed machine, to the more complex automatic types with various alternative specifications to suit requirements. In making the choice, the farmer has to consider the acreage to be planted, the labour available, as well as invariably making a compromise over how gentle the planter is with sprouted seed and its evenness of tuber spacing.

PLANTER TYPES

Conveniently, planters can be classified into six basic types in accordance with their metering mechanism.

Hand-Fed
At its simplest, the mechanism consists of a drop tube into which the 'seed' is placed by operators to the sound of a bell. The hand-assisted planter uses a segmented supply wheel into which the tubers are placed to be metered on to the ground.

Cup-Fed
The seed is collected from the supply hopper by steel or plastic cups mounted on chains or belts. Most modern planters of this type now have a twin set of cups for each row, either fixed to one single broad belt, or linked twin chains or belts. One planter has three sets of cups per row. The more cups there are, the slower the cups need to pass through the supply hopper, reducing the risk of damage to sprouted seed.

Interchangeable cups or inserts are available for some machines to suit seed size. Doubles on most machines are avoided by adjustable agitators or rubber flickers mounted on the cup units. Seed rate and spacing are controlled by adjusting the relative speed of the cups to ground speed, which is altered by changing sprockets from the ground wheel drive.

52

PLATE 3:1
Cup-fed planter mechan-
ism—twin cup

PLATE 3:2
Cup-fed planter mechanism—triple cup

Flat-Belt-Fed

This ingenious planter mechanism developed by the NIAE and produced by Howard Rotavator Co Ltd, feeds the tubers from the bulk hopper on to twin horizontal belts. The belts are angled to form a V trough on to which the line of tubers are closely spaced. By relating ground speed to belt and metering mechanism speed, spacing and seed rate are adjusted. The metering mechanism gives very accurate seed rate per hectare, but requires closely graded seed for even spacing. The mechanism is considered gentle for sprouted seed.

Moulded-Belt-Fed

Developed by Smallford Planters Ltd from the NIAE-designed machine. The mechanism is similar in configuration to the flat-belt planter, but the flat belts are replaced by a moulded cup belt. Operators are required to ensure correct filling. The mechanism is gentle for sprouted seed.

Multi-Belt-Fed

This new planter mechanism, which was developed in the Netherlands, uses 28 belts for each of the two rows that can be planted. The belts are arranged so that a trough is formed, which makes the seed tubers form a single line. The centre six belts form the planting belts and the remaining eleven each side make up the feed belts. Planting and feed belts turn in the opposite directions, leading to a single line of tubers. Spacing is governed by selection of one of sixteen gears altering the belt ground-speed ratio. A primary flat conveyor controlled from an electro-magnetic clutch, operated from a pressure switch in the multi-belt trough, feeds potatoes to the trough, controlling the rate of feed. Seed is tipped from trays, or a bulk hopper on to the primary conveyor. A soft foam-rubber roller grips individual tubers at the end of the planting belts and expels them in a controlled manner to the furrow formed by the planter share.

Finger-Fed

The flexible or metal fingers (depending on manufacturer) grasp individual tubers and deposit them near to ground level. With one planter a choice of up to three finger sizes is supplied to suit various shaped and sized tubers and even cut seed. Another finger-fed machine, which uses metal fingers, requires repositioning of pegs or wedges and adjustment of the fingers to suit the seed size. The

PLATE 3:3
Flat-belt-fed planter mechanism

PLATE 3:4
Moulded-belt-fed planter mechanism

PLATE 3:5 (*above*)
Multi-belt-fed planter
mechanism

PLATE 3:6 (*left*)
Finger-fed planter
mechanism

tubers are fed to the fingers, which are mounted on a disc, and operated by a cam mechanism to open and close at the appropriate time. The feed chambers are separate from the bulk hopper, thus keeping the movement of the seed to the minimum and keeping damage levels low.

Seed rate is adjusted by choice of sprockets from the ground wheel drive.

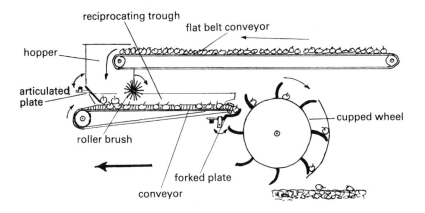

3.1 Planter mechanism for sprouted seed from France (Jeantil)

There are one or two planter mechanisms that do not fall neatly into the former classifications. The first is a French planter, designed specifically for sprouted seed. The mechanism consists of a flat-belt-conveyor which conveys the tubers to a hopper. On the hopper bottom an articulated plate senses the presence of a few tubers and stops and starts the belt conveyor. The potatoes then feed on to lower feed conveyor belts which are made up to form a 'V' trough. A roller brush and the reciprocating trough sides ensure that the tubers are aligned on the belts. At the end of the conveyor the potatoes are placed one by one on to a hinged, forked plate which, being tipped by the weight of the potato, disconnects the electro-magnetic clutch of the conveyor and stops it. The tuber is collected from the forks by a continuously rotating wheel with special cups which transfer the seed to the ground. Once the tuber is removed from the articulated fork, the conveyor is activated again and the sequence recommences.

One other mechanism is worthy of comment, although it is not used widely in the UK. This is the pick-fed planter. Basically designed for cut seed, it is suitable for whole seed, although it can not be regarded as having a gentle action. The mechanism has wheels on to which are fitted 16 arms, each containing a spike, and cam-operated discharge units. The tubers are spiked and located on the prongs; at the discharge point the prongs are retracted through a head releasing the tubers. Seed rate is controlled by a sprocket change to the selecting mechanism drive.

PLANTER MECHANISM AND SEED SUITABILITY

It is well known that damage to the sprouted seed can lead to a yield reduction, but it is more difficult to assess the effect of different planter mechanisms. It is clear that hand-fed, belt-fed (moulded, flat and multi) are kinder to the seed than some of the cup and finger-fed machines; certainly the recently introduced twin cup-fed machines are more gentle than the single cup machines they replace. But it is the condition of the seed itself, the sprouting method and the seed grading which can have an overriding effect.

Short green leafy sprouts tend to suffer less damage during planting than soft white sprouts of the same length.

Closer grading can reduce yield loss from damaged sprouts in most automatic planters. In the cup and finger-fed machines, closer grading allows the flow of seed from the bulk hopper to the cup or finger compartments to be more accurately controlled. It allows only a few sets to pass to the cups or fingers, avoiding the churning which would occur with larger quantities at this point. With the belt-fed planter, the situation is slightly different. Closer grading allows adjustment of the seed flow which reduces damage, but it will also ensure closer setting of the shutter and rollers to give uniform filling of the metering trays, leading to more evenly-spaced tubers on the ground. Closer grading of the seed for the multi-belt-fed machine also improves planter seed spacing.

A minimum of at least two grades of seed should be used with automatic planters, i.e., 32 mm–44 mm and 45 mm–51 mm, and further grades if the range exceeds 51 mm.

SPACING ACCURACY

Assessments and survey work over the last few years have established that the 'Positive' planter mechanism, e.g., cup-fed, moulded-belt and finger-fed machines, will give the most even spacing assuming the seed is reasonably closely graded. The flat-belt and multi-belt mechanism can give more varied spacing, although the seed rate is often very consistent. Closer grading and correct adjustments can give considerable improvements in spacing accuracy for these mechanisms.

Spacing accuracy is compared for different planting mechanisms by measurement and calculation of the percentage coefficient of variation. The higher the percentage coefficient, the more inaccuracy in spacing. Typical percentages for the different planter mechanisms are shown in Table 3.1.

TABLE 3.1.

Planter type	Coefficient of variation (mean) (per cent)
Twin cup-fed	27
Moulded belt-fed	30
Finger-fed	37
Multi-belt-fed	40
Flat-belt-fed	57

Some single cup-fed machines have been fitted with a 'topping up' magazine, which adds a single tuber to the cups, should there be a miss. The mechanism consists of a segmented round tray which is loaded by hand; the tray revolves and ejects a single tuber once a miss is sensed.

Monitoring is available on some planters which indicates to the tractor driver whether the individual planting mechanisms are working properly and misses are being avoided. Growers have developed their own systems which range from mirrors to lights operated from micro-switches activated by the selection mechanism.

PLANTING RATE

Overall work rate is dependent on many factors, the planter, the seed handling system, methods of pre-planting cultivations, etc. If one can get all the farm maincrop potato acreage planted within 10 consecutive working days, there is unlikely to be any yield reduction due to late planting.

With automatic planters, the spot rate of work is determined by the planting mechanism and the gentleness of planting required.

The rate of work of the twin cup machines is considerably improved over the single cup machines—allowing speeds up to eight kilometres per hour to be achieved.

The acreage potential of each planter type, given in hectares for each row of the machine for a period of 10 working days, can be summarised as in Table 3.2.

TABLE 3.2.

Planter type	Hectares/row/10 days
Cup-fed (twin)	17
Moulded-belt-fed	12
Flat-belt-fed	20
Multi-belt-fed	20
Finger-fed	17

In practice, models with a greater number of rows do not always give a corresponding increase in working rate.

ROWS AND ROW WIDTH

Planters are available with units for two, three, four or six rows, choice will depend to a great extent on the acreage to be planted. The wider the planter, the greater the volume of seed to be carried: the tractor must be man enough not only in power terms, but also in its ability to lift the planter when trailing mounted or semi-mounted models.

The modern large planter is often fitted with a bulk hopper running the full width of the machine; this prevents individual metering and hopper units following the ground contours. To avoid variations in tuber depth, it is essential to have self-levelling opening coulters and a level seed bed devoid of plough 'finishing' furrows.

On some planters, the furrow openers or coulters are spring-loaded individually and the penetration pressure can be adjusted centrally, or individually to suit ground conditions and to achieve the desired planting depth.

Row coverers are either of two types: the mouldboard ridger, or the disc coverer; most machines can be fitted with either type. Adjustments for disc and ridger width are available. Ridgers are either fixed to the main frame, or mounted on a parallelogram linkage, but discs are almost always fitted on floating radius arms.

PLATE 3:7
Ground-following sprung coulter on full-width hopper planter

PLATE 3:8
Full-width bulk tipping hopper   Hassia

Most machines are adjustable for row width from 650 mm to 900 mm. But there are a few planters where width is limited to a narrow range. Planters with individual hoppers are readily adjusted on a common frame, but full-width hopper machines require adjustment of the hopper sides, which can be a long job with some models.

HOPPER TYPE AND SIZE

When considering the purchase of an automatic planter, the system of handling the seed should be borne in mind. Models can be purchased with small feed hoppers only, with a storage area for trays or even a trailed platform behind the planter when used entirely for earlies and sprouted seed. Large hoppers that run the full width of the machine facilitate the use of bulk handling methods. The height and accessibility of the hopper to operators and equipment must be considered.

Hopper capacity will decide the field length permitted with a hopper full of seed. This can present problems where field lengths are great and require two filling points in the field.

There are two main hopper types: the full-width or individual hoppers for each row. To give sufficient capacity, these hoppers are mounted high above the opening share, the filling height being at high level. Recently large capacity tipping hoppers have become available, allowing easy filling from ground level and ideal for bulk handling. During planting these hoppers are tilted by means of hydraulic rams. This ensures that a shallow layer of potatoes is presented to the selection cups, avoiding the feed cups having to pass through a dense layer of tubers and thus reducing damage to the sprouts during planting.

SEED RATE AND PLANTER ADJUSTMENT

The seed is a major cost in the growing of potatoes and must be used effectively and efficiently. It is the maximum economic return from the crop that is important. Seed rate is determined by the number of seed tubers to be planted per hectare and the average weight of the individual tuber. The tuber weight and the set numbers have considerable and interacting effects on crop yield and the size grading of the ware tubers; these effects are dependent to some extent on the variety of potato grown. Tables are available from The Agricultural Development and Advisory Service giving the optimum populations and seed rates for various varieties based on the seed size (sets/50 kg) and the ratio of seed cost to the anticipated value of the ware.

Once the desired population has been determined, the spacing within the row can be worked out. The fairly small change in spacing between tubers along the row which has to be made to maintain the same set population if the row width is changed from 730 mm to 900 mm has comparatively little effect on crop yield or grading, so the same plant population may apply to any of the normal row widths.

Seed spacing can be determined from the following formula:

Seed spacing along the row (mm)

$$= \frac{10,000,000}{\text{Row width (mm)} \times \text{plant population (1,000 sets/ha)}}$$

Adjusting for seed rate on most planters is straightforward and usually involves a change in sprockets on the drive chain, the manufacturer providing in the handbook a range of spacings to suit various sprocket combinations. It is usual for there to be a speed range limit, certainly for the positive cup-fed and finger-fed machines when using very close spacings within the rows.

Interchangeable cup inserts or fingers are available for some machines to suit seed size. Close grading of the seed will produce more even spacing in the ground, and reduce damage to sprouted seed.

HANDLING SEED POTATOES

The choice of system for handling seed potatoes must depend on a number of factors:
● labour available
● acreage to be planted
● whether seed is sprouted or not.

Controlled sprouting will involve handling the tubers into the store whether this is a glasshouse or a controlled environment building, removing it from store in the spring, and transporting to the field and planter. This takes time and a great deal of labour, certainly when conventional chitting trays are used.

The introduction of high-speed automatic planters in recent years has highlighted the inefficiency of traditional handling methods. Hand-fed planters travel at about 1·6 km/h, so the time spent filling the planter is not significant overall. With high-speed automatic planters which can travel at speeds up to 10 km/h, filling time by traditional methods can account for up to 50 per cent of planting time. To make use of their full planting potential, improved seed handling is essential.

TABLE 3.3. **When planter filling time is cut by half with a high-speed planter the benefit is a 22 per cent increase in work rate, but with a slow planter only 5 per cent**

Speed km/h	Planting minutes	Fill	Turn	Work rate ha/h
1·6	33	5	3·3	0·21
1·6	33	2·5	3·3	0·23
10	5·5 5 3·3			0·64
10	5·5 2·5 3·3			0·78

Seed Handling System

There are four major systems of potato seed handling using various types of container and systems of operation (the bracketed letters refer to examples shown in Fig. 3.2):

1. Tray systems
   - conventional trays (A)
   - trays on pallets (B)
   - trays into bulk bucket (C)
   - trays into bulk box (D)
2. Sacks on pallets (E)
3. Bulk container
   - mesh crate (F)
   - shelved box (G)
   - pallet box
4. On floor to trailer (H).

Tray Systems—Conventional Trays

About 60 per cent of potato growers in the United Kingdom are using trays and it is still the most suitable container for sprouting seed. Trays are made of wood or polythene and are normally 750 mm long, 450 mm wide and 150 mm deep. Each will hold about 16 kg of seed (normally three trays to 50 kg).

The system has the greatest labour/time content of up to 120 man minutes/tonne for filling the trays and from 10 to 20 man minutes/tonne for filling the planter.

3.2 Potato seed handling systems

Trays on Pallets

This is the next stage in improving seed handling. Special skeleton two-way entry pallets are available with dimensions to suit the base area of four trays (1,500 mm × 900 mm). Trays can be stacked in layers seven to ten high. The central four posts of the top layer

PLATE 3:9
Seed handling—bulk bucket tipping seed into planter

of trays can be wire-tied for stability during transit. This system eases movement of trays within and out of store, but does not speed up tray filling or planter-filling time.

Trays to Foreloader Bucket
The next two systems speed handling into the planter but involve double handling of the seed tubers.

The technique relies on the trays being tipped into the forklift or fore-end loader bucket in the field while the planter is still planting. The bucket can then be tipped into the planter at the headland at a rate of 4–5 man minutes/tonne. One man can keep a 4-row high-speed planter moving. It is of course useful to be able to vary the amount of tubers tipped into the planter-hopper as row lengths vary.

A bucket with a controlled hydraulic tipping action is an advantage allowing careful transfer of seed to the planter-hopper.

Trays to Bulk Box
In the chitting house seed is transferred from the trays into a half-tonne bulk box. The box should not be too deep, be wide enough to suit the planter-hopper, and have a bottom gate for tuber discharge. Planter-filling time is short, but extra labour is required in the store for box filling. The efficiency of transporting the tubers is improved as the trailer will carry an increased capacity.

Sacks on Pallets

Keeping the seed in sacks or nets means that either the seed must be delivered late, or it must be stored and possibly sprouted in bags—this is often difficult to do successfully without forced ventilation and refrigeration.

Filling the planter using sacks is quicker than using trays, but not as speedy as a bulk system. Filling times of up to 10 man minutes per tonne have been recorded.

Bulk Containers

Handling seed in bulk reduces the labour requirement and speeds handling at all stages. The main **advantages** over trays can be outlined as follows:

- Planter filling time reduced to 3–5 man minutes/tonne compared with 10–20 man minutes/tonne for trays.
- Filling the containers and putting into store takes less time (40 man minutes/tonne compared to 120 man minutes/tonne).
- Bulk containers can take less room within the store.
- Trailers can be used more efficiently, enabling larger loads.
- Handling with forklifts avoids manual work.
- Cost of containers can be less than trays.

There are disadvantages:

- With some containers sprout control can be difficult, requiring refrigeration and forced ventilation.
- Inspection for diseased tubers is difficult.
- Bulk systems of chitting often do not offer the yield advantage of tray chitting.

Mesh Crate

The mesh crate is a commercial bulk chitting container developed from the crate originating at the Terrington Experimental Husbandry Farm and manufactured by Coningsby Metals Ltd. The crate with dimensions of 1,500 mm long, 910 mm wide and 940 mm high will hold approximately 525 kg of seed. It is made with an angle-iron outer frame with weldmesh sides and has a removable liner of mesh which forms vertical pockets into which the tubers are placed. Light and ventilation can enter through the vertical gaps between the pockets.

Crates with side-opening gates are available as well as units suitable for inversion tipping.

The containers can be used in conventional chitting stores and provide a complete mechanical handling system from store to

PLATE 3:10
Seed handling—emptying a mesh crate into the planter hopper

planter. It is however essential to maintain good control over the store environment; long sprouts will result in chit damage and difficulties with emptying the crate can be experienced.

Shelved Pallet Box

This slatted wood container is fitted with two side opening gates, one above the other. The box is divided into two sections with a central shelf which can be removed to allow the bottom layer to be filled. To avoid uneven chitting, the container should not be overfilled, but an adequate gap left for ventilation. Because the layers of tubers are deeper than those of trays, illumination to some tubers is poor; good ventilation and temperature control is essential.

The container has dimensions of 1,485 × 935 × 882 mm and will hold about 500 kg of seed. When handling into the planter the forklift must have adequate tilt for the tubers to flow out of the gates or a forward tippler must be used. A three-tier box is also available giving an increased capacity.

PLATE 3:11
Seed handling—emptying a shelved box into the planter hopper

Pallet Boxes

Pallet boxes can be used for handling into the planter and are suitable for mini-chitting seed if air can be forced through the box to give even temperatures; refrigeration is almost always necessary. A number of systems have been developed in recent years to give through ventilation to standard half-tonne or tonne slatted boxes.

On Floor to Trailer

With the advent of the large full-width hoppers on planters, it is possible to tip tubers into the planter using a high tip trailer. Where seed is unchitted or the tuber eyes are just open the system may be possible, but a reduction in yield over traditional sprouting is to be expected. A controlled environment store would be necessary.

Planter filling time is short at 2·4–3 man minutes per tonne.

Other Methods of Planter Filling

Systems of seed handling and planter filling are not limited to those mentioned above. One automatic planter has a large platform on to which can be stacked trays or bags, which can then be fed into the planter as it progresses up the field. A front-mounted platform on the tractor, or a forward control tractor (*e.g.*, County, Unimog), does allow further storage of seed where planter hopper capacity is limited or rows are long.

One farmer has made use of the large full-width tipping hopper of the planter to tip seed from a pallet box with a front gate, the

PLATE 3:12
Box tipping method—forward tippler

PLATE 3:13
Box tipping method—rotary head tippler

PLATE 3:14
Planter Carrier enables additional seed tubers in trays or bags to be carried with the planter

R. J. Herbert Engineering

pallet box being placed within the hopper. This is fine until row length does not match up with box capacity, but if the box is filled at the headland during planting, two or more boxes being used then the system has potential. Perhaps a manufacturer may consider it worthwhile designing a planter with two interchangeable demountable hoppers which can be changed over when the planter requires filling. This would avoid double handling the seed and give a quicker filling time!

Handling Equipment
Most of the equipment used for handling the seed tubers may be already in use about the farm—the tractor fore-end loader, tractor forklift attachment or rough terrain forklift truck.

A hand pallet truck is inexpensive and is very useful for moving pallets about difficult buildings.

Boxes, pallets or crates can be tipped by two basic methods: the forward tippler which allows the seed to pass over the top front edge of the container or the rotating head which completely inverts the container, normally to one side. With the latter it can be difficult to control tipping and keep drops to the minimum.

Planter Hopper Capacity

Hopper capacity decides the distance the planter travels between refills; it can be as much as 1106 m with a hopper capacity of 350 kg per row or 275 m with only a 100 kg hopper. A large hopper capacity will reduce total filling time. The planter hopper must suit the handling system; complete full-width hoppers are more suitable and should be wider than the fore-end loader bucket or box pallet.

TABLE 3.4. Containers for storing and handling seed potatoes

Type	Capacity (kg)	Cost (£/tonne)	Planter refill time (man min/tonne)
Trays: wood	16	75	10–20
plastic	16	120	—
Fore-end loader bucket	350	—	4–5
Mesh crate	525	from 117	3–5
Box pallet with gate	500	32	2·5–4
Shelved box	500	50	3–5

There is a seed-handling system to suit most farms and to fit in with existing sprouting methods. Bulk storage and handling does offer some considerable advantages, but it should only be considered with the full knowledge of the possible yield reductions and with a store that can provide a closely controlled environment.

ORGANISATION AT PLANTING

Efficient and speedy planting will depend to a large extent on the organisation of the various tasks required during the planting period. Pre-planting cultivations often take place directly in front of the planter, and to avoid planting delays sufficient capacity must be available. To economise on tractor use and labour dual mounting of the powered cultivator and planter have been considered. Where sufficient front pto capacity is available, the powered cultivator can be mounted in front of the tractor and the planter behind. Alternatively, the planter can be mounted on a three-point linkage directly behind the cultivator tandem fashion.

If stone separation or windrowing techniques are to be used, there can be a delay in planting, although the separation methods may reduce the number of cultivations required. To reduce the delay problem, a number of combined stone windrowers and planters have been developed. One prototype machine manufactured by Reekie Engineering has a two row cup-fed planter mounted above the separation web of the stone windrower. The seed tubers are fed down from under the cup metering mechanisms to the opening shares by a series of compartmented conveyors which maintain the desired spacing. There is considerable platform area on the machine for stacking trays or sacks of seed tubers. Another machine has the planter mounted directly behind the stone separator achieving the same effect, but making the machine rather longer.

Field layout is important for efficient planting; the aim should be to achieve the longest row length with the hopper capacity in order to keep total filling and turning times to the minimum. The planter should be able to go up and down the row to allow the hopper to be refilled from one part of the field.

Fertiliser application at planting has cultural advantages but does entail a further operation during planting. If fertiliser is applied at planting, it is important that this does not delay the planter. Fertiliser hoppers are often placed in very inaccessible positions, requiring considerable agility in reaching them. Front mounting the fertiliser liquid tanks or granule hoppers on the tractor counterbalances the weight of the planter and eases turning at the headlands. Further information on fertiliser application is given in Chapter 4.

Chapter 4

THE APPLICATION OF CHEMICALS FOR THE POTATO CROP

CHEMICALS ARE applied to the potato crop at various stages: before, at, and after planting; on the foliage; and on the tubers. They will be in the form of granules, dusts, liquids, fogs, mists and as fumigants. The choice of method of application and how well it is done will determine to a great extent the successful use of these chemicals.

FERTILISER

Fertiliser is normally applied at planting as there appears to be little advantage in top dressing the potato crop throughout the season. There are various methods of application and placement of fertiliser. Choice of method will to a certain extent depend on the levels of fertiliser used; there is, however, a trend in the UK towards placement where approximately 50 per cent of the fertiliser is applied in this way, with the rest being broadcast on to the ploughed land before secondary cultivations.

The methods of broadcasting fertiliser liquids and granules are well known and common to many crops. The use of this equipment will not be discussed here. It is, however, possible to achieve a degree of placement with broadcasting by first forming the ridges, broadcasting the fertiliser and then splitting back the ridges. The seed is next to the fertiliser without being in direct contact with it.

Fertiliser Placement
There are a number of systems that have been developed to apply fertiliser at the same time as planting. In each case the systems have been designed to place the fertiliser near to the seed without touching it.

Granular fertiliser can be successfully applied in twin bands in front of the planter share and yet achieve an adequate incorporation with the soil within the ridge. For each potato row a hopper with twin outlets from a dual metering mechanism feeds to a broad share which makes a shallow furrow with the fertiliser deposited in bands to each side. The units can be mounted in front of the tractor pulling the planter. The planter share runs down the centre of the furrow digging deeper and throwing soil over the bands of fertiliser on each side of the furrow. The soil and fertiliser mixture is then ridged over the seed without the fertiliser touching it. The front-mounted hoppers are fitted to a framework which can be lifted hydraulically out of work. The ground wheel drive to the metering mechanism is lifted clear of the ground, at the same time disconnecting the drive. Front mounting has one major advantage: the weight of the unit and fertiliser will balance out the weight of the planter and not be an additional weight on the rear of the tractor. One difficulty is the effect on the steering of the tractor when planting. The fertiliser shares, being forward of the steering wheels, tend to steer themselves, causing the complete unit tractor and planter to 'crab' with subsequent misalignment of the fertiliser bands and the planter shares. The technique can be applied, however, directly in front of the planter, the hoppers and fertiliser shares being positioned between tractor and planter.

The fertiliser granules can be applied at the planter share. Drop tubes from the metering mechanism set well in front of the tuber drop position deliver a band of fertiliser into the furrow bottom; soil enters over the fertiliser from holes positioned in the 'furrow opener' sides, thus protecting the tuber from direct contact. Alternatively, the fertiliser can be applied after the tuber has been sown and before covering. Two drop tubes positioned each side of the tuber feed into tine coulters which penetrate just below tuber depth. There is little risk with this method of fertiliser coming into contact with the seed, but it does mean that the hoppers are in the way of loading the planter.

The fertiliser metering mechanism will generally be of the external force feed type, *i.e.*, a gear type rotor. Feed rate is normally controlled by rotor speed adjusted by sprocket change from ground wheel or planter drive.

Liquid fertiliser allows the holding tank to be mounted away from the planter—either as saddle tanks or positioned forward of the tractor radiator, the liquid being pumped to the placement position. This has the advantage of counteracting the weight of the planter as well as placement at the seed drop position. Liquid injection can be made each side of the tuber into the formed ridge or before the coverers. The liquid metering pump can be driven

PLATE 4:1
Filling a liquid fertiliser tank mounted in front of the tractor and planter
combination

from the planter ground wheels, and thus rate of application will
always relate to forward speed.

SPRAYING

There are four major operations for the sprayer in the potato crop:
weed control, pesticide and fungicide application and haulm dessication. Herbicides for weed control are either applied before
planting and then incorporated into the soil as in the case of couch
control, or applied to germinating seedling weeds before the potato
shoots emerge from the soil (pre-emergence). Among the main
pests of the potato crop are aphids; systematic insecticides may be
applied to them as granules or as sprays, which can also be combined with fungicides for blight control. Fungicides are normally
applied at short notice as a protective control against blight when
the weather conditions indicate a blight risk. Blight control by
haulm dessication, which also facilitates lifting, is carried out by
spraying with chemicals, such as Reglone or sulphuric acid; the
latter is the quickest and most effective but requires special acid-
proof machines.

Except for the application of acid, standard conventional sprayers can be used. Late application of fungicides can be successfully
applied with aircraft at ultra low volume (20–30 l/ha). This avoids
the damage and losses which would arise from late application on
lush crops with ground machines.

This is not the place to go into the basic design of the agricultural sprayer, but to emphasise some aspects of sprayer design that should be borne in mind when choosing a sprayer for the potato crop. Spraying for potatoes will be applied at high volume (700 l/ha to 1,000 l/ha) and at low volume (200–350 l/ha) and the sprayer should be easily adjusted to meet these requirements. The choice of boom width for the potato is important in that the larger the boom, the fewer the wheelings and the faster the rate of work. If the acreage and field size justify a large boomed sprayer, there are two main disadvantages. First, the extra weight of the sprayer and tank must be supported by suitably large wheels which enforces the argument for wider row width (900 mm). Secondly, the wider the boom, the greater the problem of boom 'whip' or 'bounce' due to the up and down movement of the tractor or trailed sprayer wheels which is accentuated at the end of the boom. In recent years sprayer manufacturers have been improving boom suspension systems, with, for example, the 'balancing' spray boom, where the centre of the boom is supported from above, similar to a pendulum. The sprayer can tip from side to side over rough ground without seriously affecting the boom. Shock absorbers dampen any swing that may result. Another system uses a suspended beam linkage on the parallelogram principle which achieves the same effect.

Sprayers suitable for sulphuric acid require to be resistant to acid corrosion with all parts coming into contact with the spray. Sprayer tanks are normally stainless steel with special bodied diaphragm or centrifugal pumps. Contractors normally carry out acid spraying.

SPRAYER CALIBRATION

Calibration should always be carried out at the beginning of every season, after every 100 hectares and after a change of tractor or wheels, nozzle tips or operating pressure.

The procedure for sprayer calibration is as follows:
1. Check chemical packs for any special instructions, then choose an application rate within those recommended (e.g. 200 litres per hectare).
2. Choose and fit nozzle tips to operate in their acceptable pressure range appropriate for the chosen application rate and anticipated forward speed.
3. Carry out a trial run with the sprayer tank half full of water spraying on a surface similar to the average on which you will spray. Check that the proposed forward speed gives an accept-

able level of boom bounce and boom yaw (back and forth movements) and the gear selection gives a pto rev/min. of about 540.

4. On the same surface check tractor speed:
   (a) In midfield mark out a distance of 100 m with two canes (pacing is not accurate enough—use a tape).
   (b) Select the gear and engine rev/min. as in (3).
   (c) Measure the time taken to travel 100 m spraying at the selected engine rev/min. Start and stop timing as tractor knocks canes over.
   (d) Refer to Table 4.1 to check the approximate forward speed in kilometres per hour.

Table 4.1.

Time in seconds	120	90	72	60	51	45	39	36	33	30
km/h	3	4	5	6	7	8	9	10	11	12

   (e) Return to yard. Adjust spraying pressure to the level recommended in the chemical instructions and/or within the nozzle chart range.

5. Check nozzle spray patterns and alignment visually, replace any rogue nozzle with a nozzle matched to the flow rate of others in the group.

6. Compare individual nozzle outputs by nozzle flow measure or recording time required to fill a measure to a predetermined level. Replace any nozzles more than ±5 per cent from the average.

7. Turn 'Spray On' to clear air from the boom, then 'Switch Off' pump. Ensure the tank is level and fill it with clean water to halfway up the neck of the tank—mark the level inside the neck front and rear.

8. With the sprayer stationary and the tractor rev/min. at the setting used when the forward speed was checked, spray out for the time taken to travel 100 m in 4(c).

9. Refill the sprayer to the marks in the neck with clean water, using a calibrated measuring vessel or flow meter.

10. Establish the effective swath width of the sprayer in metres (*i.e.*, the distance between a pair of nozzles times the number of nozzles).

11. Compare the quantity of water required with that shown on the calibration chart (Table 4.2) for the chosen application rate and the effective spraying width of the sprayer.

TABLE 4.2. Sprayer calibration chart (Agricultural Training Board)

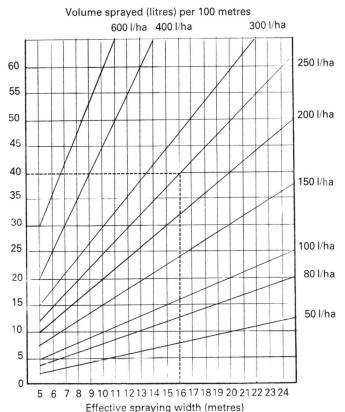

Volume sprayed (litres) per 100 metres

Effective spraying width (metres)

Example: Shown by dotted line a sprayer with a width of 16 m at 250 1/ha should deliver 40 litres over 100 m test-run.

12. If the rate is not correct:
   ● make small adjustments by varying pressure (N.B. Do not go outside chemical and/or nozzle tip recommendations);
   ● make large adjustments by changing nozzle tips.
13. Recheck after each adjustment until correct.
14. Record for future use:
   ● nozzle tips fitted
   ● application rate
   ● spray pressure
   together with information from 4(e), and date of check.

Equipment checklist
Tractor.
Sprayer (having undergone pre-season preparation).
Tractor instruction book.
Sprayer instruction book.
Sets of nozzle tips, spares and instructions.
Small measuring vessel or nozzle flow meter.
100 m tape and two canes.
Large calibrated measuring vessel or hose flow-meter.
Calibration chart.
Watch (with sweep second hand) or stopwatch.
Supply of clean water.
A hard level surface.
A typical field with a 100 m run.

Electronic Aids
There are many new electronic aids for spraying coming on to the
market: flow-rate recorders, pump output control linked to forward
speed, acremeters, etc. These units can assist the operator, but as
a start the most important aid is an accurate speedometer.

GRANULE APPLICATION

The application of granules to the potato crop is for the control
of pests and of nematodes. Chemicals such as Oxamyl and Aldi-
carbore for aphids and eelworm; Disulfoton is for aphids and
Carbfuran for eelworm only; Phorate is for aphids and wireworm.
These chemicals are applied in two ways, overall with incorporation
and in the furrow at planting.

Application rates are normally very low for granule application,
for example: 11 kg/ha of Phorate in the furrow at planting. Typical
rates for Aldicarb and Oxamyl for potatoes for overall application
are 56 kg/ha and 33·6 kg/ha respectively. Application rates will,
however, vary with soil type. Most of the chemical manufacturers
issue setting tables and information for the well-known applicators;
all machines should be calibrated in the field prior to application.

Most of these chemicals are highly toxic and for the protection
of wild life must be covered or incorporated immediately after
application. With land-wheel-driven applicators drive to the metering mechanism can continue after the unit has been raised out of
work, leaving the granules on the soil surface; this may not be
serious where granules are to be incorporated, but should be noted
and the simple devices to raise the drive wheel at or before the
planter is taken out of work should be used.

Micro-granule Applicators

The low application rates require special micro-granule applicators or modified fertiliser spreaders. One of the well-known manufacturers of granule applicators in the UK is Horstine Farmery Ltd. The standard Micro-band unit consists of three to five hoppers, each with twin outlet tubes. Each hopper has two metering units of the external force-feed type. For overall application the hoppers are mounted on a framework and are ground-wheel driven from a common shaft. The hoppers can be mounted on the front of the tractor allowing combined application and incorporation with a rotary cultivator. For overall application of nematicides fish-tail outlets can be fitted.

Rate of application is adjusted by a choice of rotor size, number of rotors per outlet, and choice of pullies (driver and driven). Rotors are available in aluminium, alloy or plastic. Choice of rotor will depend on granule formulation. Chemical manufacturers' instructions on this aspect should be followed.

These hopper units can be planter mounted to apply the granules into the furrow bottom next to tubers (*e.g.*, Disulfoton for aphids control).

Various manufacturers produce granule applicators of a similar type with individual hoppers but different metering mechanism. Rate of application in most cases is adjusted by choice of ground drive gearing.

Also available are pneumatic fixed-width granule applicators. Horstine Farmery manufacture two models: the TMA2 and TMA4. These units use a metering mechanism similar to the Micro-band model, but it feeds into a fan unit which distributes the granules to nozzles on the boom. The nozzles have impact plates to spread a width of 1·2 m depending on material. Total spreading widths are up to 12 m with up to eight nozzles.

Some fertiliser spreaders are suitable for overall granule application—particularly the pneumatic machines. These machines are available with a range of boom widths, a typical spreading width being 12 m. Most types have similar metering mechanisms, each distribution tube and nozzle having its own metering unit. A high-pressure fan provides the air blast for distribution, and impact plates or 'butterfly' spreaders fitted at each nozzle scatter the granules. Some spreaders can achieve the low application rates without modification—where required, modifications include alternative low-rate metering units. Varying application rate on nearly all machines is achieved by a stepless variable speed drive from the wheels to the metering units.

Various spinners and oscillating spout fertiliser broadcasters can be used, but low-rate application kits are normally required. In fact, some farmers have successfully used grain drills with spouts removed to broadcast the granules.

Granule Incorporation
The granule manufacturers have specific recommendations for the incorporation of their product. Most granules, where applied over-all, require to be evenly distributed throughout the topsoil. Oxamyl and Aldicarb granules should be incorporated using a rotary cul-tivator or power harrow (*e.g.* Roterra, reciprocating harrow) at a working depth of 100 mm with a forward speed of 3–5 km/h. One pass should be sufficient. Where unpowered implements are used, *i.e.*, disc harrow, Dutch harrow or spring tine, a working depth of 150 mm is required, with a speed of 6·5–10 km/h. Two passes are recommended, with the second pass preferably at right angles to the first. On soils of a high organic content it has been found that powered rotary cultivation is necessary for best results.

APPLICATION OF CHEMICALS TO THE POTATO TUBERS

Chemicals are applied to the potato tubers for sprout control and for the treatment and control of storage diseases. There are two main types of chemicals used for sprout suppression: Chloropro-pham (CIPC) and Propham (IPC). Both these related chemicals are marketed in liquid formulations for application as a fog into the ventilation ducts of bulk stores. CIPC is also marketed as granules, primarily for application to box-stored potatoes at the time of loading. Tecnazene (TCNB) is usually applied as a dust or as granules to potatoes as they are loaded into store. Not only is Tecnazene a sprout suppressant but it is also used for control of dry rot in both ware and seed potatoes. 2-Aminobutane, for the control of diseases such as gangrene, skin spot, silver and black scurf in seed potatoes, is marketed as a liquid for use as a fumigant. Thiabendazole (TBZ) is a wettable powder fungicide which is applied at an ultra low volume mist to potatoes as they are loaded into store, the intention being to dampen the tubers lightly all over without over-wetting them. For best results the fungicide should be applied as soon after lifting as possible.

Thermal Fogging Machines
Fogging describes a technique which relies on chemicals being

heated and struck by a high-speed blast of air or gases which break it into very small droplets in the 4 : 40 micron range. There are two main types of equipment: the pulse jet foggers and the exhaust foggers. The former is the name given for a group which operate on an engine similar to the V2 rocket, the chemical being injected from a pressurised container directly into the hot exhaust blast from the motor. Machines of this type are the Pulsefog, Swingfog and Dynafog. Exhaust foggers are similar and achieve the same effect but with a different layout. Two or four-stroke petrol engines drive a friction pump of low efficiency which produces heat which raises the temperature of the chemical, while transferring it from the tank to the nozzle. The exhaust then breaks the chemical and distributes it. Machines within this group include the Dorman, London and Burgess machines. When operating these foggers care is necessary because the exhaust gases and exhaust chambers are very hot and inflammable material such as straw can easily be ignited. Where it is necessary to fog near a straw wall, an asbestos pipe can be inserted into the duct and the fogger operated clear of the straw. Make sure a fire extinguisher is readily available. Typical application rates with foggers would be up to 18 l/h.

Another type of fogger uses a low-speed fan blowing a stream of air over a vaporising unit—basically a hot-plate. The chemical flow rate is measured in drops per minute—normally a flow rate of 60–80 drops per minute is sufficient.

Rotary Atomiser

Various types of rotary atomisers are used. There are the hand-held machines which have a spinning disc revolving at more than 7,000 rpm, producing fine droplets of 60–100 microns. A fan unit producing a turbulent air blast distributes the mist; this unit can be used for some formulations of sprout suppressants. The other type is used for the application of fungicides into store at ultra-low volume. This unit which consists of an electrically-driven high-speed disc, is mounted over a roller table or at the end of a conveyor to provide a fine mist to cover the tubers completely. Application rates are in the region of 2 l/t. A suitable tent or cover is required to enclose the misting area.

Misting Nozzle Applicators

The storage fungicides can be applied at various points before the crop is in the store. One manufacturer (Delavan) supplies a misting nozzle applicator that can be fitted on the harvester at the end of

PLATE 4:2
Store elevator with automatic swinging head filled with Delavan 'Storite'
application at head

C. J. F. Fyson and Son Ltd

the picking-off table or the discharge elevator, or positioned at
the store on a roller table elevator, or even box filler. The standard
unit consists of supply tank, two swivel-mounted non-drip nozzles,
high-pressure pump and control valve and pressure gauge. Positioning of the nozzles is important to achieve overall application;
for example at a conveyor or elevator discharge point one nozzle
will be aimed up under the discharging crop and the other down
from above. Different sized nozzles will be required for differing
flow rates of tubers. A pneumatic mister is also available.

Dorman produce a similar unit which can be mounted in various
positions. Also available is a gravity feed unit which uses a fan jet
with an air nozzle disrupter. The air requirement is $8 \cdot 5$–12 m^3/h
at about 2 bar. Most normal air pumps for tyre filling can be used.

With any of these misting systems, it is essential that the tubers
do not become over-wet. Where the application point is over a
bulk of potatoes, it is necessary to switch off the misters if the
tuber flow is interrupted. Various systems have been developed
to do this; basically they consist of a flap or rubber probe which
rides over the tubers on the conveyor. If the tuber flow ceases, the
flap or finger drops, cutting off the supply to the mister nozzles.

A mixture of TCNB and TBZ can be applied with these misting
systems to give a dual control of sprouting and a range of diseases.

Dust and Granule Application into Store
In the majority of cases, these are applied manually with a long-handled scoop. For large tonnages automatic vibratory feeders can be used to apply an even coating of granules or dust on to the potatoes as they pass along the store-filling conveyors. Rate of application can be adjusted to match the tonnage into store. It is essential with TCNP and CIPC granules to get an even distribution over the tubers for good sprout control.

SOIL FUMIGATION METHODS

Soil fumigation treatment is carried out to reduce the nematode content in the soil. The chemical used is 1·3-dichloropropene. (Telone).

There are three basic systems available.

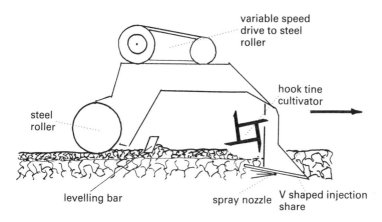

4.1 Sub-surface fumigant inspection for soil sterilising—machine component parts

1. *The sub-surface fumigant injector* (Rumptstad Combiject). With this type, the liquid fumigant is sprayed evenly beneath 'V'-shaped injector shares, which cut a slice of soil the full working width of the machine to a depth of 180–200 mm. A hook-tine rotary cultivator crumbles the soil surface to a fine tilth, which is then levelled by a levelling bar. The depth of cultivator is adjustable. The soil surface is sealed with a powered roller. The pressure and speed of the roller can be adjusted to achieve optional sealing and avoid surface cracking. A compressor supplies air to tanks of

fumigant which supply the liquid under pressure to the nozzles underneath the shares. Calibration is done through a choice of nozzle size, injection pressure and tractor speed. Working widths are 2·25 m or 3 m with an average work rate of 1 ha/h.

2. *The plough sole applicator.* This inexpensive gravity-flow or low-pressure system which can be mounted on straight or reversible ploughs, applies the fumigant into the furrow as the soil is turned by the plough share.

3. *The Tine Injector.* With this method the liquid fumigant is metered via drop lines attached behind toolbar-mounted chisel lines, knives or heavy-duty cultivators. Tines should be no more than 300 mm apart and should penetrate the soil to at least 200 mm or preferably 300 mm depths.

The effectiveness of any soil fumigant treatment must depend on the degree of incorporation and the length of time the volatile liquid and gases remain within the area to be treated; sealing of the top surface is essential with the soil type and its moisture content being important factors in achieving this.

Chapter 5

IRRIGATION

OF ALL the arable crops, potatoes are the most likely to give an economic return for investment in irrigation.

For both early and main crop potatoes, the availability of irrigation gives the grower some control over one of the factors which affects both yield and quality of the crop. How great is the need for irrigation is determined by the climate, soil type and whether early or main crop potatoes are being grown.

Any irrigation system requires a high degree of management to obtain the best results and traditional systems make regular and often unwelcome demands on farm labour. More modern systems substantially reduce the labour demand, but the need for careful supervision remains.

However carefully the costings on irrigation are calculated, there is still a large risk factor. The return on a big capital outlay can come quickly if dry years follow the installation and the opposite can be the case if there are a succession of wet years.

CROP RESPONSE TO IRRIGATION

Clearly, it is impossible to give exact figures, but the average yield increase in response to irrigation on a well-managed crop in an area of established irrigation need will be in the order of 0·08 t/ha per millimetre of applied water. This figure will be similar for early or main crop potatoes.

As well as a yield increase, there can be other unquantifiable advantages, such as beneficial effects on quality and continuity of production and marketing. Also, there can be the factor that in years of drought, when potatoes are in short supply, a grower with irrigation will be able to make the most of the high prices.

Potatoes should be irrigated from the time the tubers are the size of marbles, providing there is a soil moisture deficit of 25 mm or more.

The soil moisture deficit (SMD) is the difference between the actual transpiration of the crop in a given period and the rainfall during the same period, assuming that initially the soil was at field capacity. (Field capacity is the point at which if there is any further rainfall, it is lost through the drainage system).

Different soils hold different quantities of water, therefore potatoes on a heavier soil are able to withstand a higher SMD without coming to harm than potatoes on a lighter soil with less available water.

It is normal to apply 25 mm of water at one application on a rotation of ten days. The estimation of the area which irrigation can cover is normally done on the assumption that 25 mm will be applied at an application on a ten-day rotation.

The maximum rate of application of water varies with soil type from 13–20 mm/h for coarse sand to 5–9 mm/h for silty loam and less than 4 mm/h for silty clay. These figures are for bare soil and can be increased when there is full crop cover. Great care is needed when the potato ridges are still exposed and as small a droplet as possible should be used. Fields should be checked for ponding or run-off and modifications made to equipment if required.

Estimation of how much irrigation is required is a highly complex matter, but the latest method from the Agricultural Development and Advisory Service is a simple practical system for irrigators.

The farmer must have a rain gauge and record accurately the daily rainfall. With the average transpiration figures and irrigation applied, a running record of the SMD is produced. Each week actual transpiration figures are available from local ADAS offices, calculated accurately by the Meteorological Office based on the prevailing climatic conditions for that week. This system enables the grower to plan his irrigation for the coming week. More information on this system is available from ADAS offices.

SOURCE OF WATER AND STORAGE

There are three basic sources of water for irrigation: public supply, ground water and surface water. Public mains supply is too expensive, so there are only two sources of water to be considered for irrigation of potatoes.

The Water Authority can give advice on both ground water and surface water sources of water. A borehole supply (ground water) is normally the most economical source of water as it occupies only a very small area of ground because there is no storage. Boreholes are only possible with certain geological formations and even then a licence must be obtained from the Water Authority.

It may be possible to extract water directly from a surface water source such as a river or pond throughout the year, but in many cases an abstraction licence will not be given for this, or it is prohibitively expensive. For this reason, growers installing irrigation are building reservoirs which can be filled in the winter from surface water sources for summer use.

Reservoirs

In most cases a farm reservoir is made by excavating and embanking earth. Approximately $1·8 m^3$ of water can be stored for every $1·0 m^3$ excavated. It is important to choose a site where the soil itself will form a reasonably impermeable seal as a lining will increase the cost of storage by a factor of as much as five.

The most common linings which are used are butyl rubber, pvc or polythene. It is normal practice, when the lining is in place, to cover it with a thin layer of soil as this will cut down the risk of a puncture. Most liners degrade in the sunlight, which is another reason for covering them with soil. Approximately $1·0 m^2$ of liner is required for every $1·5 m^3$ of water stored.

In estimating the capacity required, it is normal to allow an extra ten per cent for evaporative losses, and for unlined reservoirs another ten per cent for seepage losses.

It is recommended that a civil engineering consultant, with experience in reservoir construction, is employed. If in excess of $22,730 m^3$ of water is stored above the natural level of any of the land adjoining, it is obligatory, in the UK, that the reservoir be designed and constructed under the supervision of a civil engineer.

DISTRIBUTION SYSTEM

Any distribution system needs careful planning so that the right quantity of water, at the right pressure, is delivered to the irrigator. The constituents of a distribution system will consist of some, if not all, of the following: permanent pump, portable booster pump, permanent mains and portable mains.

The permanent pump will be at the reservoir or water source and probably will be housed in a pump house. These pumps are normally electrically driven if three-phase is available or driven by diesel engine. They are typically of single stage centrifugal design capable of producing pressures of up to 6 bar. For higher pressures, more than one stage is necessary. The pump must be able to cope with the intended capacity with a safety margin of at least twenty-five per cent. (A hectare millimetre per hour is $10 m^3/h$.)

As most modern mobile irrigators require water at pressures of 6–7·5 bar at the machine a booster pump is sometimes required, particularly if the original system had been installed to cater for conventional sprinklers needing only 4·0 bar. Quite often this booster pump will be tractor-driven. It is important to install an engine protection unit because the tractor will be operating unattended and in the event of cooling or lubrication failure, the engine could be irreparably damaged.

Most permanent mains are buried and it is important to record exactly where they are placed. Diameters of permanent mains typically range between 100 mm and 175 mm.

Portable mains are normally in 6 m lengths of aluminium pipe with quick-fit couplings. These pipes are not strong and need to be handled with care. They will certainly not withstand a tractor driving over them. The standard sizes are between 75 mm and 150 mm.

As water flows through a pipe there is a pressure loss due to friction and the higher the flow rate through a pipe of a given diameter, the greater the frictional loss. The frictional loss is also directly proportional to the length of pipe through which the water flows. Therefore the size of pipe required for an irrigation system must be carefully chosen. Table 5.1 may be of use in estimating the size of pipe required.

Table 5.1. Guide to internal pipe diameter (mm)

Flow in	Length of pipe (m)			
litres/second	0 – 150	150 – 300	300 – 600	above 600
2·0	50	62	—	—
4·0	62	75	75	—
7·5	75	75	100	—
10·0	75	100	100	—
15·0	100	100	125	150
20·0	100	100	125	150
22·5	100	125	150	150

Example 5.1
Consider an irrigation system where 5 ha/mm are applied per hour and the distance of pipework is 400 m.

$$5 \text{ ha/mm per hour} = 50 \text{ m}^3/\text{h}$$

$$50 \text{m}^3/\text{h} = \frac{50 \times 1,000}{3,600} = 13 \cdot 88 \text{ l/sec}$$

Therefore, from Table 5.1 the pipe size of between 100 mm and 125 mm can be read off. A pipe size of 125 mm would be chosen.

Irrigation pipe comes in four different classes depending on its ability to withstand pressure:

	A	B	C	D
Maximum working pressure bars	3	6	9	12

Many old systems with conventional sprinklers are class B or C and so if modern self-propelled irrigators are being considered new pipework may be needed. Booster pumps near the irrigator itself can overcome this problem by boosting the flow to the required pressure. This use of booster pumps can only be made if the existing mains can take the flow of water needed without giving frictional losses above class B or C capability.

TYPES OF IRRIGATION EQUIPMENT

Conventional Sprinkler Systems

The standard system of portable rotary sprinklers with lateral aluminium pipes is laid out from a mains supply. The sprinklers and pipelines have to be moved three to four times in a 12–16-hour day. This is a labour-intensive system of around 6 man h/ha which is not very popular as it is tedious and pipes have to be carried through wet potato haulm. This system does have a low capital cost, around £900 for a line capable of irrigating 0·4 ha at a time. The drops produced are acceptable right the way through the growing season and there is a good distribution efficiency.

An adaptation of this system in order to cut down on some of the labour is the alternate sprinkler system needing around 4·25 man h/ha. Sprinklers and standpipe are fitted on to alternate connections at any one time and then moved to the intermediate position. This means that the pipework has only to be moved half as often, although a greater length of pipe is required than in the first example. All the connections to the lateral pipes have automatic closing valves which only open when a standpipe is installed. Although this system reduces the labour requirement, it costs nearly double the first example.

Another adaptation is to have the lateral pipe system installed for the season and just move the sprinklers and standpipes when required. Clearly, this considerably reduces the labour, but has a high capital investment of over £700 per hectare, which is unlikely to be economically viable for the potato crop.

These sprinkler systems operate at a pressure of around 4 bar.

MOBILE IRRIGATORS

Pivoted Rotating Boom Irrigators

The two types of pivoted, rotating boom irrigators are either with a boom supported at the centre which rotates every 1½ to 2 minutes or with a long boom supported at various points and rotating about one end. This second type is unsuitable for potatoes as the wheels supporting the boom go around in a circle and would therefore have to go across the ridges.

The central pivoted irrigator produces a circular wetted pattern, the centre being stationary as irrigation takes place. These machines can apply 25 mm in four hours and, typically, are moved four times a day. The irrigator has to be moved over land which it has already irrigated.

One difficulty with this type of machine is that the wetted pattern is altered by strong winds and there is little that the operator can do to rectify this problem.

There are some designs of machine which under-irrigate the centre of the wetted area.

The droplet size spectrum generally contains a proportion that are of a size that may cause soil damage under some circumstances. It is worth checking on this point before purchasing such equipment.

These machines operate at between 5·5 and 6·5 bar; an average labour requirement is 0·75 man h/ha.

Mobile Raingun-Based Irrigators

Rainguns are characterised by large jet sizes, (15–20 mm, compared with 5 mm in sprinkler systems), high operating pressures, and large wetted areas from single jets. They may be static, particularly for organic irrigation purposes, or more often sledge- or carriage-mounted.

The sledge-mounted rainguns use a lightweight sledge which is dragged through the crop by the actual supply hose which is wound slowly on to a drum at the headland. Different application rates are achieved by varying the drum speed. The drum is normally driven by a water-driven mechanism which requires a water pressure of 7–11·5 bar. To be moved the drum and sledge are towed behind a tractor. At the new site, the tractor pulls the sledge to its field position, unwinding the hose from the drum as it goes.

With the cable-hauled system, the raingun is on a carriage. A cable is used to pull the carriage along, rather than the supply pipe itself. The winch is again water-powered, requiring a pressure in

PLATE 5:1
Conventional sprinklers on the potato crop

PLATE 5:2
Drum winding gear for hose-reel raingun

the order of 6 to 7·5 bar. Different application rates are achieved by varying the winch speed. As a cable is used rather than the supply hose to pull the raingun, it is possible to travel a distance the length of the supply hose on either side of a central supply point at one application. A separate hose reel, driven by tractor pto, is usually used to lay down and rewind the flexible hose.

With both types of rainguns water distribution can be good, providing attention is paid to operating pressure. Lane spacing will have to be varied to suit the wind conditions. The larger rainguns available, in particular, produce big droplets and should only be used for irrigating crops with full cover.

The pressures at which both sledge and carriage-mounted machines operate are higher than are used in conventional sprinkler systems. Therefore, it is important to ensure that the pump can produce sufficient pressure to operate a raingun. If a conventional sprinkler system is being replaced by a raingun, an additional pump will be needed.

There is a large range of raingun-based irrigators on the market, irrigating from 1·0 ha to around 8 ha with 25 mm of water per day with two runs. Prices in spring 1980 ranged from £3,500 to £11,000 per complete irrigator.

An average labour requirement is 0·5 man h/ha.

Mobile Sprinkler-Based Irrigators
The mobile sprinkler based system has a fixed boom, with rotating sprinklers mounted on a carriage which also takes the hose drum. The carriage is propelled in the same way as the cable-hauled raingun *i.e.*, by a winch powered by the water pressure (6–7 bar) which pulls the carriage across the field.

With the smallest model in the range, the hose can only be rolled up, but with the other models the carriage can move the length of the supply hose either side of the central supply point at one application, by winding up and then unwinding the hose. The machine will stop automatically at the end of its run, which can be set at either when the drum is fully wound, or fully unwound, depending on field layout. The pipe can be wound on to the drum using the tractor pto.

This irrigator can be used with a raingun instead of a boom with sprinklers.

The prices in spring 1980 are from around £3,400 to £10,000 per unit. The range goes from 2·4 ha per day up to 6·4 ha, assuming two runs a day and application of 25 mm of water.

PLATE 5:3
Mobile sprinkler-based irrigator

Self-Erecting Sprinklers

This system consists of standard rotary sprinklers attached by swivelling brackets to a 75 mm diameter layflat 'fire hose'. The sprinklers, which are at intervals all down the hose, fold down so that the hose can be wound on to a drum.

The drum is attached to the rear linkage of a tractor and the hose is laid out as the tractor is driven down the field. When the water comes on, the sprinklers pop up. In order to rewind the hose on to the drum, the tractor reverses up the field. The drum is hydraulically driven.

The water distribution is similar to a conventional sprinkler system.

The pressure required is around 5 bar and the sprinklers will apply 25 mm in about three hours.

The labour requirement is approximately 0.75 man h/ha and the cost of the basic machine in spring 1980 was £2,500.

Table 5.2. Summary of irrigation equipment

Type of irrigator	Area irrigated/ setting (ha)	Capacity (ha)	Operating pressure (bar)	Labour Requirement (man h/ha)
Conventional sprinklers	0·4 +	13+	4·0	6
Self-erecting sprinklers	0·35+	14+	5·0	0·75
Rotating boom	0·5–1·2	16–38	5·5–6·5	0·75
Mobile sprinkler-based system	1·2–3·2	19–51	6·0–7·0	0·5–0·75
Mobile raingun-based irrigators	0·5–4·0	8–64	6·0–7·5	0·5

Area irrigated/setting assumes an application of 25 mm.
Capacity is taken to be the area irrigated in a ten-day cycle, assuming an 80 per cent field efficiency.

Chapter 6

HARVESTING

SUCCESSFUL HARVESTING is essentially dependent on the cultural practices applied to the land and crop before harvest starts. Many of these aspects are mechanical and have been discussed in previous chapters. Harvesting is an engineering problem and requires the separation of loose soil, clod, stone and trash from the potatoes. For a crop of 50 tonne per hectare, 24 tonne of soil and rubbish has to be separated from each tonne of potatoes harvested and this must be carried out as gently as possible to keep damage to the minimum.

The period of time available to harvest potatoes is limited. In the first place, sufficient growing time must be allowed for the crop to 'bulk up' and produce the yield, but also the tubers must be lifted before weather conditions make harvesting difficult and crop temperatures are low, leading to increased tuber damage. On individual farms the competition with other crops for time and labour during this critical harvesting period will put a further constraint on the time available. The acreage, soil conditions, labour and time available in addition to the crop's intended use, are all factors which must be considered in making the choice of harvesting system.

HAULM DESTRUCTION

Haulm destruction is carried out to control tuber blight and to facilitate lifting. Destruction is by chemical 'burning off' or by pulverisation and very often a combination of both methods.

The haulm pulveriser can be harvester mounted or trailed by a tractor. Most machines use flails to lift and chop the tops. Long and short flails are used to fit into the shape of the ridges and allow the haulm to be lifted from the furrow bottom. The flails which are usually free to swing are attached in banks to a horizontal shaft which rotates at approximately 1,800 rpm. The tractor-trailed machines are usually semi-mounted so that the complete machine can be lifted at the headlands. Depth wheels which are fully adjustable for row width assist in maintaining the machine's lateral position as well as giving adjustment to the cutting height. The machines are normally suitable for two potato rows and fully adjustable for rows of 650–900 mm spacings. Harvester-mounted units can be of similar design and mounted directly in front of the lifting share.

HAULM PULLERS

Over recent years a number of haulm pullers have been developed, principally for the seed potato crop. Most machines have a two-row flail topper mounted on the front of the machine or tractor which matches the ridge profile and is set to leave sufficient stem for the rear-mounted puller to grip.

There are two versions: the rubber belt and the pneumatic wheeled puller. The belt machine has two sets of belts per row. The pair of belts are arranged down the row with the driving shafts vertical. The front end is funnel-shaped to allow the haulm to be gripped between the sprung-loaded belts. The belts run backwards faster than the forward speed of the tractor, thus gripping, pulling and discarding the haulm at the back. The wheeled puller has two pneumatic wheels per row; the wheels are on almost vertical driven shafts angled forward with the wheels in contact. Haulm feeds between the wheels which run backwards faster than forward speed, the haulm is gripped, pulled and discarded.

Working speeds of about 6 km/h are quite possible. Depth control is usually by ridge-following 'diablo' rollers.

POTATO LIFTERS

Potato lifters remove the tubers from the ridge and place them on the surface for hand picking. Within this category there are three basic lifter types: the spinner, the reciprocating riddle and the elevator digger.

Spinners
In the past, spinners were usually trailed and driven by a land wheel, but most machines in use now are tractor-mounted and operated by the power take-off (pto). The machine consists of a number of metal tines which are mounted on a rotary cage which maintains them in a vertical position. The cage revolves, passing the tines through the ridge at right angles to the row and throwing the tubers on to the soil surface. An adjustable screen prevents the tubers being thrown too far. The potatoes are initially lifted

by a share. Speed of rotation of the spinner must be limited where the soil is dry and friable. Soft rubber tine covers can be used to reduce bruising of the tubers. One disadvantage with the spinner is that not all the tubers are well exposed.

Reciprocating Riddle
This lifter uses a full one-piece share on to which are attached closely-spaced tine bars which feed the tubers on to a reciprocating riddle which separates the soil from the tubers and then discharges the tubers to the ground. Generally, these machines are only suitable on the lighter soils.

Elevator Digger
Elevator diggers which are trailed or semi-mounted are available for single or twin-row harvesting and suitable for row widths from 650 mm to 900 mm depending on model. The lifter has a broad flat raising share, behind which is an elevator chain constructed of parallel steel rods running on adjustable agitators. The fine soil is shaken through the links of the chain and, in good lifting conditions, will place a soil-free row of potatoes at the rear of the machine. Most machines are now fitted with a long angled primary web and short horizontal web at the rear. Choice of chain link or Continental separation webs are available and fitted with rubber covers to the bars for crop protection if required. Various web gaps are available; for example, a pitch gap of 24 mm for earlies and a 41 mm gap for main crop harvesting in wet conditions.

Share depth is controlled by either combined pneumatic or steel depth control wheels and disc coulters. Each type is adjustable for depth through the screw jack principle.

The rear of the implement is mounted on two pneumatic tyred jockey wheels which allow the semi-mounted unit to swing and turn at the headlands. A high output harvesting system has been developed from the two-row elevator digger. By using one straight through lifter with a further two lifters discharging to right and left, a windrow of potatoes from six rows is formed, which is harvested by a purpose-built harvester. Harvester rates of up to four hectares/day are possible.

COMPLETE HARVESTERS

The continual decline in the numbers of regular and casual farm staff used on farms has speeded the development and introduction of complete harvesters. In the United Kingdom over 55 per cent of the 1976 crop was harvested entirely by machine. The use of unmanned harvesters on suitable soils and on soils which have been modified by stone treatment (see Chapter 2) has increased over the last few years.

It is clear that the reduction in the potato acreage on the more marginal soils and the increased acreage of potatoes on individual farms with suitable soils has contributed to this trend.

Unmanned harvesters used under ideal conditions of a light soil with freedom of clod or stone can operate at work rates of up to 0·5 ha/h (for a two-row machine) without any hand work at all. Under more difficult conditions workers are required to pick off clod, stone, etc., on the machine, or on the handling line into store. When examining potato harvesting in general it is therefore important to place the equipment in the context of a harvesting system and the conditions under which it will operate. It should be remembered that few if any complete harvesters can work satisfactorily under really wet, heavy soil conditions.

Machine Classification
The range of complete harvesters available can be classified under the headings shown in Table 6.1.

TABLE 6.1. Classification of harvester types

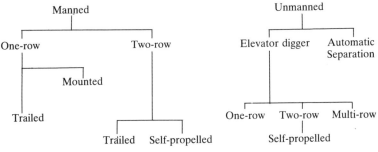

Whatever a machine classification it has to carry out a number of tasks which are common to all machine types and it is in this area of separating crop from material of similar size and weight where these mechanisms differ. The complete harvester digs, separates and delivers into sacks, boxes or trailers during one pass of the machine over the field. Most harvesters, manned or unmanned, are based on the elevator digger principle which uses a digger blade share, and a rod-type elevator web. The share lifts and shatters the ridge then transfers the crop and soil on to the first elevator web where soil is removed by sieving. The next stage is haulm removal which separates loose and attached top from the tubers. At this stage most harvesters employ a separation device which can be mechanical, as on the unmanned machines, or using operators on the manned harvesters, or a combination of both systems.

Tubers then pass direct to the discharge elevator and into the trailer, or a bunker hopper, sacks or boxes. It is essential that the complete operation is carried out with the minimum of damage to the crop. Before examining the relative merits of the various harvesting systems, the major components of a complete harvester are outlined.

The Share and its Components
The most widely-used share is the flat blade, available as a single piece 'A' blade or in two or three sections for each row. The single piece 'A' share is often recommended for strong heavy soils where the tubers are lying deep and excess clod on to the primary web must be avoided. Round shares of this type are also available which will tend to lift a broad section of the ridge without going too deep and are useful with shallow crops and on light soils where not sufficient soil is available to cushion the crop on the main web. Split shares in two or three sections allow greater filtration of the soil. Thus unnecessary soil is not carried on the web, and under weedy conditions, particularly with 'twitch' (*Agropyron repens*) clogging of the share is reduced.

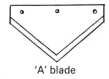 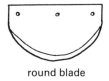 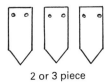

'A' blade   round blade   2 or 3 piece

6.1 Typical share types

The pitch angle of the share can often be adjusted on most machines to increase or decrease the digging effect of the share—normally little adjustment if any is required from the manufacturer's initial settings. At each side of the shares are fitted discs or torpedoes. These cut or lift surplus trash and haulm away from the share blade. Under light soil conditions the discs can fail to rotate. Scalloped discs, or on some machines powered discs, are available to overcome this problem.

Rotary shares are available on some harvesters and these do offer certain advantages over the fixed share, although they are more expensive to produce. Powered contra-rotating disc shares lift single or twin rows on to the elevating web and will reduce draw-bar pull by about 30 per cent compared with rigid shares. Tuber damage with this type of share is often less than with the blade share and it is a share type which does offer potential for high-speed low-damage harvesting.

Reduction in share draft can be obtained by vibrating the fixed share through the soil. Some experimental work has taken place in America on this aspect and there is likely to be further development in the future.

One machine, the Faun potato harvester, uses a combination of the conventional share and a powered vertical wheel with rubber flails. The wheel angled across the ridge rotates and passes the soil and crop from the share on to a rotating disc. This method moves the soil at right angles to the ridge for the transverse elevating web. The system has proved in practice to have a low damage record.

Share depth control is important so that tuber damage is avoided and excessive soil and clod are not transferred to the elevating webs. With most harvesters the shares and the front section of the web are carried on a floating chassis. This chassis is raised and lowered for share depth control by various means, the most common method being the 'diablo' depth roller. Over each ridge is mounted a convex roller, by linkage or by hydraulics the height of the ridge controls the depth of the share. Most systems of depth control attempt to reduce the downward pressure of the depth rollers so that the weight does not deform the ridge leading to unrealistic depth control in soft soil conditions. Depth is adjusted by a screw jack device on the roller linkage.

One manufacturer (Hestair Harvesters) uses a servo-hydraulic depth control system. The digger share is controlled by a small pneumatic wheel running on top of the row being lifted. The wheel is connected through a servo-device to a double-acting hydraulic ram which automatically lifts or lowers each share according to the action of the wheel on the ridge top. Depth is adjusted by a screw on the end of the spool valve linkage.

On the smaller less expensive harvesters, a steel flat-band depth wheel running at the side of the ridge is used. Depth is controlled by a simple screw jack.

PLATE 6:1
Powered disc share on prototype harvester from the Scottish Institute of
Agricultural Engineering

PLATE 6:2
Faun mounted potato harvester showing transverse webs

Primary Separation

On most machines the primary separation takes place on the digger
web. This consists of an endless web or rods—often rubber or pvc
covered—with a gap from approximately 24 mm for earlies to
40 mm for main crop on heavy wet land. The standard web gap
for most situations of main crop harvesting would be 35 mm.

Oversized rod covers can be used to reduce web gap in some situations. This may be necessary in light soils and dry conditions when the soil can be lost almost immediately from the web and the soil cushioning effect on the tubers is lost.

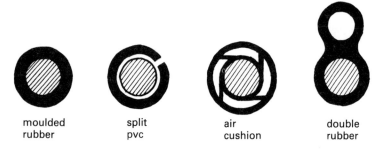

moulded   split   air   double
rubber   pvc   cushion   rubber

6.2 Types of web rod covers

There are two basic types of web used on harvesters, the chain link and the Continental web. The chain-link web consists of separate rods with chain links at each end which interlock with each other to form a flexible web of rods evenly spaced throughout. As the link chain wears, the space between rods will increase leading to increased tuber loss. Two link types are available: the 'ups' and 'downs' which when used as alternate rod links provide pockets in the web; this reduces tuber roll back on the steeply angled webs. Various covers are available for chain-link webs—moulded-rubber covers, split pvc, pillow cushion and double rubber covers. The covers will reduce the rod spacing and assist with tuber damage reduction.

The Continental web is similar in that it is made up of rods, but they are fixed by rivets at a set spacing on to fabric band of webbing at the extremities of each rod. Various covers are also available for the rods of the Continental web.

The length of the primary separation web and the bed angle are important as these determine the separation area available and the length of time the tubers remain on the web. Steep-angled webs without soil can lead to unacceptable roll back of tubers. On some harvesters web angle can be adjusted using a steep angle in heavy wet soil conditions and a less steep angle in dry, free-flowing soils.

Web speed is important in terms of the amount of soil separation that takes place and the amount of damage caused to tubers (to be discussed later in the chapter). On many harvesters the speed of the web is determined by the speed of the tractor engine, or by a sprocket change. It is often impossible to obtain the correct ground speed pto relationship to achieve optimum performance and least damage with only one gear ratio from pto to web speed. Many machines offer a two-speed input to the harvester gearbox from the tractor pto shaft for normal and slow web speed. Other machines require a sprocket change. Infinitely variable web speed is considered to be an advantage in order to achieve optimum web speeds under variable soil conditions. A number of harvesters are now fitted with either variable-speed hydraulic drives or a drive system using a 'V' belt and variable diameter pulley.

One of the problems of having a long primary web is that its speed and web gap are the same throughout its length. This means that its gap and speed must be a compromise between high speed for soil separation and low speed for damage prevention. By splitting the main web, the first section can be run at high speed with a larger gap in the web, giving greater soil separation without increasing tuber damage or loss of small tubers. The second section can be run at a slower speed for gentle handling without the soil cushion, and the closer web gap will reduce small tuber loss.

All harvesters are fitted with a means of agitating the main web to increase soil separation. On some machines the amount of agitation can be varied by simply moving a lever on a ratchet quadrant. The standard agitator mechanism relies on an eccentric toothed sprocket which meshes with the rods of the web; by moving this sprocket nearer the web the throw is increased, moving it away and out of mesh with the rod, and agitation is reduced or removed. Plain rollers can be used for no agitation on some machines. With less expensive harvesters interchangeable agitator sprockets of different sizes to suit agitation required are used, with plain rollers for no agitation. Agitation should be used with discretion, especially in dry, cloddy conditions. It should only be used to assist the sifting of soil through the main web and not to try and break up clod.

On many machines, particularly unmanned harvesters, crop or haulm retarders are used. There are various types, but basically they are rubber fingers or paddles which are positioned over the top of the main elevator web and mounted on cross-bars which can be turned to angle or remove the retarders impinging on the crop. The fingers are staggered on the bars to disturb the crop without causing blockages.

Retarders are used where the tubers are hanging on the haulm and particularly where the potatoes are harvested green and where the tops are not pulverised.

One machine fits the retarder tines to a conveyor system which allows the tines to pass over the main elevator, retarding the crop without causing blockages. Another type uses oscillating tine retarders which move forwards and backwards through the crop.

Crop Elevation

On manned and some unmanned harvesters it is necessary to convey the crop to a higher level on the machine for manual or mechanical separation. To do this there are a number of elevating methods:

● Rotary cage
● Duplex elevator
● Flighted elevator.

The most widely used elevating method is the rotary cage elevator. The open cage is devoid of a centre shaft and radius supports

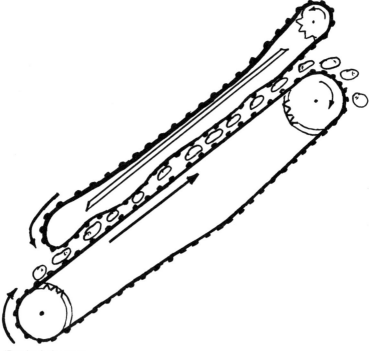

'Duplex' elevator

6.3 Potato elevation on the harvester; Duplex elevator

and revolves on jockey pulleys about its circumference. The tubers pass into the lower half of the drum and are then conveyed up the circumference of the cage by internal rubber-covered paddles, the tubers being discharged at the top on to the picking-off table or separating mechanism. The cage consists of an open framework using closely spaced rubber or plastic-covered steel cables around its circumference which allow soil to be sifted through the spaces and provide gentle handling of the tubers. Under heavy, wet soil conditions there is a tendency for the drum to be clogged up with soil.

The Duplex elevator used on machines manufactured by Hestair uses two Continental webs, one above the other. The bottom web is in a fixed position top and bottom and runs on side runners. The top or 'over-run' web is driven by a sprocket at the top, but has no lower sprocket. The tubers are elevated between the two webs, the top web retaining the tubers in position and preventing roll back. Cleats and/or weights can be fitted to the over-run web to assist the elevator when working uphill which exaggerates the elevator angle.

There are various flighted elevators used on harvesters. The most common type uses a broad Continental web elevator with rubber cleats. They are more often seen on two-row manned harvesters. The elevator initially runs at a slight angle so that the tubers are contained on the elevator cleats, but at the top the web is angled forward to discharge the tubers on to the 'picking-off' table.

The other major elevator type is similar in operation to the rotary cage elevator, the cleats being on the inside of the web, the web passing around the end of the primary web and the picking-off table. The tubers are elevated up on one side only, the other side returning the empty cleats to low level.

Where angles are not too steep conventional webs with cleats can be used. Design of elevators and conveyors for harvesters is important to prevent tuber damage. There is little soil present at this stage to cushion and to protect the tubers. Soft rubber covers are available to cover elevating bars similar to those shown for the digger web. Various designs for transferring tubers from one elevator or conveyor to another to keep damage to the minimum are discussed later in the chapter.

HAULM SEPARATION

The design and operation of the haulm removal devices on harvesters is particularly important with varieties of potatoes where the tubers are firmly fixed to the stolons. Crushing and surface damage to the tubers must be avoided. Haulm removal is often followed by a haulm stripping device. There are three major types of haulm removal mechanism on harvesters today; these can be classed under the following headings although there will be minor design difference within these classifications:

● Web and roller with haulm guides
● Fingered elevator and paddles
● Haulm web remover and stripping rollers.

Web and Roller with Haulm Guides

This is a fairly simple device fitted to the majority of unmanned harvesters. The device positioned at the top of the primary or secondary web consists of a plain steel roller located directly beneath the top sprockets of the web and contra-rotating with the web causing material to be fed between the bottom of the web and the roller. Some adjustment for roller position is available on most machines. Sprung or weighted curved guide tines encourage haulm and weeds to pass between roller and web.

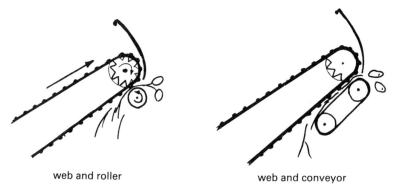

web and roller   web and conveyor

6.4 Haulm separation on the primary and secondary web

Long haulm can wrap around the roller; this can be avoided by replacing the roller by a short conveyor which has a total length greater than the haulm length.

Fingered Elevator and Paddles

This device is situated between the main web and a rear haulm elevator. A fluted roller collects potatoes and clod and transfers it to the bottom of the haulm elevator and into the elevator drum.

The trash and haulm pass over the fluted roller and are collected by the rubber fingers on the haulm elevator web and carried over the top of the elevator and on to the ground behind the machine.

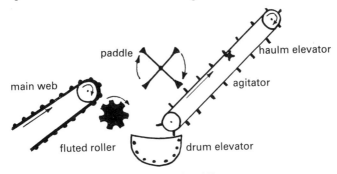

fingered elevator and paddle

6.5 Haulm separation

To avoid potatoes attached to the haulm going over the top, adjustable, spring-loaded paddles 'comb' the haulm as it passes up the elevator. A mechanical agitator provides an additional shaking action on the elevator web. The rubber fingers and the web bars are covered with air-cushioned rubber to protect tubers.

Haulm Web Remover and Stripper Rollers
At the end of the main web a haulm remover web is positioned so as to allow the crop to fall through the spaced bars whilst catching the haulm and rubbish being elevated by the digger web.

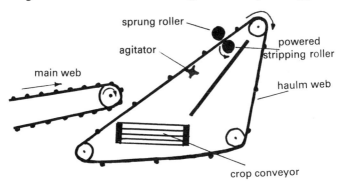

haulm web and stripping rollers

6.6 Haulm separation

Potatoes that remain attached to the haulm usually hang below the haulm web. The web passes through two rollers one on top and one beneath. The top roller is adjustable forward and back and spring-loaded. The bottom roller is powered and will strip the tubers from the haulm. An agitator shakes the web to encourage the tubers to hang through.

Another type worthy of mention uses twin rubber-ribbed steel rollers which draw the haulm from the web and strip it from the tubers. This system is used on harvesters where the rollers are used as deflectors to change crop direction.

CLOD CRUSHERS

A number of machines have facilities for crushing and breaking up soft clod. At its simplest it may consist of closely spaced rubber fingers lying across the main web, which tend to press the soil through the bar gaps. The finger pressure can be adjusted, but the system must not be used to deal with hard clod.

The clod-crushing roller has an adjustable gap and is spring-loaded. The object is to set the roller spacing wide enough to dispose of as much clod as possible without losing usefully sized tubers. Under stony conditions the roller might be forced open so that good potatoes are damaged and lost. In these conditions the roller gap should be closed.

Popular on unmanned harvesters are a series of coil-spring type powered rollers which will assist with clod breakage and soil separation. The 'star' wheel soil extraction system is to be found on some specialist harvesters. All these devices require careful setting to avoid tuber damage in dry loose soil conditions and particularly where stones or hard clod is present.

Stone and Clod Separation
The next operation on the manned machines is the separation of stones and clods which may be the same size as the tubers. This may be done by hand—the potatoes, stones and clods etc., being delivered to a suitable sorting belt. Operators pick either stone and clods or potatoes, whichever is the greater, and place them on to a parallel conveyor.

Partial or complete separation of stones and clods can be achieved before the crop reaches the pickers. Mostly the partial separation methods rely on the difference in shape, roughness or density of the potatoes from the unwanted material to make their mechanism work.

Partial separating mechanisms:
- Inclined conveyor
- Pintle conveyor and deflector
- Rotary brush and pintle conveyor.

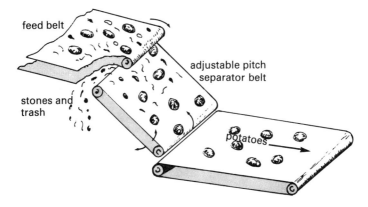

6.7 Stone and clod separation—inclined conveyor (plain or pintle belt)

The inclined conveyor separation system uses the round shape of the tubers to help separation. Tubers pass from a conveyor on to a high-speed inclined endless belt. The potatoes roll down to the pick-off conveyor, angular clod/stone and trash are conveyed up to the trash side of the system. The angle of the endless belt can be adjusted to suit conditions and the type of trash present. Pintle rubber conveyors have been used to provide location for the trash rather than the plain belt.

On some separation mechanisms of this type the inclined conveyor runs in a direction across the incline and the direction of the tuber flow. It is essential with this type to have a studded or pintle belt.

The next two types of separating mechanism are very similar and rely on the shape and weight of the different materials passing on to the separation conveyor. The conveyor which is often slightly inclined across its direction of travel is made on modern harvesters from rubber belting with very small rubber flexible studs and is normally referred to as pintle belting or the hedgehog. The stones and angular clod will tend to sit firmly on the belt and will not be dislodged by the brush or deflector. Small pieces of trash will also be conveyed away, the potatoes with the assistance of the brushes or deflector rolling down the slight incline.

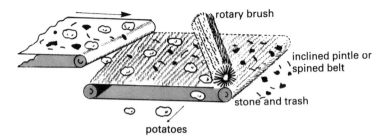

6.8 Stone and clod separation—rotary brush and pintle conveyor

The brushes are made of nylon or similar materials and can normally be raised or lowered over the conveyor bed. If too many potatoes are going through the brushes are lowered. Brush and conveyor speed can be adjusted to suit the conditions and to give the best separation possible. The deflector mechanism uses a rubber-fingered comb which is angled and will oscillate back and forth.

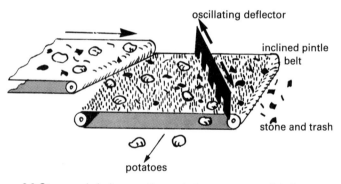

6.9 Stone and clod separation—pintle conveyor and deflector

The height above the conveyor, the deflector angle and its degree of oscillation can be adjusted depending on the quantity and size of stone present and the size of the tubers. The incline of the pintle or hedgehog conveyor can be adjusted: the greater the number of stones, the less steep the angle.

COMPLETE SEPARATING MECHANISMS

There are two major systems available on harvesters at present:
● The electronic separator
● The airlift separator.

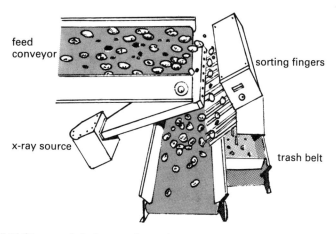

6.10 Stone and clod separation—electronic x-ray separation mechanism: principle of operation for static and harvester sorters

With the electronic system X-rays are used to distinguish between clods, stones and potatoes. The crop material is fed evenly through X-ray beams which will activate pneumatically-operated sorting fingers allowing the unwanted stones and clods to pass through and the potatoes to be diverted to the discharge elevator. The X-ray beams are blocked by the more dense material, *i.e.*, clod and stone, but large potatoes can also block the beams and the device has a sensitivity control which can be adjusted until the large tubers are retained. This control will not require readjusting until a change of crop with a different maximum size is encountered.

The separating mechanism can only deal with a set number of objects in a given time, so it is possible to overload the device by passing too much crop material through it. It is also possible to under-utilise the separating device by not feeding the material fast enough. For the most efficient operation of the mechanism, forward speed of the harvester would need to be varied continuously. In fact, the Scottish Institute of Agricultural Engineering have developed a mechanism that controls tractor forward speed from the impulses of the X-ray mechanism to achieve optimum running conditions. In practice, the driver must note the material going into the trailer and being discarded to achieve optimum forward speed. Room is available for a picker on the harvester at the trash discard belt and he is able to remove large tubers or overload material. It may well be economical to accept some overloading and to use the picker to achieve optimum running conditions.

The air-lift separating mechanism relies on a high-powered engine-driven centrifugal fan unit to suction-lift the tubers from the stone or clod. A chain bar conveyor supplies the mixed material to the suction chamber, the tubers are lifted to a power-driven conveyor across the air vent which prevents produce being sucked into the fan. The tubers are conveyed out of the suction area on the underside of the conveyor until they are released. The separator can be adjusted for crop condition by flaps on the air chamber inlet

PICKING-OFF TABLE

This is an important area on any manned machine, for the conditions under which an operator works will tend to affect the efficiency of sorting. An operator is not comfortable if it is necessary to stretch more than 450 mm to the centre of a picking-off table. Therefore the siting of discharge conveyor or chutes and crop conveyors is important. On many machines there is the facility either to remove clod, stone and trash from tubers or to remove potatoes from the trash, whichever is the greater. Picking-off table conveyors can be of plain rubber belt, Continental web with bars and linked chain. On some machines with rod or link chain conveyors, drop links are provided to allow trash to escape from within the conveyor web.

SIZERS

Where tubers are going off the field in bags direct to market sizing is often required on the machine. Sizers of various types are fitted to harvesters as standard or as optional extras. Spool and endless chain sizers are the most common and will be covered more fully in Chapter 8.

CROP DISCHARGE

There are four basic methods of discharging potatoes from manned and unmanned harvesters. These can be listed under the following headings:
● Discharge elevator
● Intermediate hopper and discharge elevator
● Bunker hopper
● Bags and boxes.

PLATE 6:3
Large conveyor belt sorting table on harvester allowing easy reach for operators

Discharge Elevator

The discharge elevator must convey the potatoes to the trailer with the minimum of damage to the potatoes. Most modern harvesters are fitted with 'swan neck' discharge elevators which can be lowered into the trailer to reduce tuber drop. Hydraulic control of discharge is almost universal except on the cheaper machines and will either raise and lower the complete elevator or just the last discharge section. Unfortunately no harvester manufacturer has thought it worthwhile to manufacture a self-compensating height control for the harvester discharge elevator. The SIAE have developed such a device which will limit automatically the drop height to such a level at which damage is unlikely to occur.

Also on the market are all the components and technology for such a mechanism, but any system developed must be combined with a suitable elevator breakaway device. In fact this lack of a breakaway device on the normal discharge conveyor is the reason generally given for not lowering them fully into the trailer.

Most harvesters now use a Continental web with deep rubber flights which both elevate and control the fall of the tubers at the discharge end.

PLATE 6:4
Bunker hopper on single-row harvester

Intermediate Hopper and Discharge Elevator

The discharge conveyor can be combined with an intermediate or 'hold over' hopper with a capacity of up to 350 kg for a two-row machine. This allows the harvester to operate during the time the trailers are being changed. Careful design is necessary here to avoid large drops into the hopper bottom.

BUNKER HOPPER

There are two types of bunker hopper used on harvesters—the tipping and the moving floor bunker. Bunker hopper capacity will vary but with a single-row machine is approximately 1·25 tonne and for a large two-row machine up to 2·5 tonne. The object of the bunker hopper is to allow the harvester to work without the trailer running alongside continuously. This means that where store distances are small one man can carry out potato haulage and the trailer can be left at a suitable point in the field convenient for the harvester to discharge.

The bunker hopper is necessarily fairly deep inside in order to contain the tonnage of tubers and some form of cushion is necessary to avoid damage during filling. Discharge of the bunker is considered to be an area where damage can occur and tuber drop must be kept to the minimum. With the hydraulic tipping bunker this is more difficult as the hopper must be raised to a high level to tip into the trailer. The moving floor bunker hopper does reduce this problem by fitting special rubber chutes and restricting webs at the discharge point but it is still a critical area. One manufacturer has managed to combine the bunker hopper with the advantage of a swan neck elevator (Grimme Jumbo).

BAGS AND BOXES

Most manufacturers offer bagging platforms for their manned harvesters with twin-spouted bagging weigher units which allow continuous filling. Two-row models have a double set of weigher units. An adequate bagging platform is essential for storage of bags preferably on pallets for quick turn-round at the headlands. Many machines can be adapted for bagging, the discharge elevator being removed and replaced with a grader and weigher/bagger unit. It is possible to fit the bagging unit within the bunker hopper of some harvesters. A pallet fork device is available to fit on some harvesters to allow the pallet to be discharged on the move.

By clearing the bagging platform of the weigher unit, it is possible on some harvesters to fill pallet boxes, but it is essential to have some method of reducing the drop into the box.

The Harvester Running Gear

Every harvester, unless supported by the tractor, must have wheels and where they run and how they operate can affect the efficiency of harvesting.

The lighter, smaller machines do not require large-diameter, wide wheels to support their weight and the fact that the wheels travel in the furrow bottom does not cause a problem of tuber damage; however, with heavier machines it is essential that the wheels are kept from the furrow. Two-row machines have sufficient width to mount the wheels under the main web, the self-propelled machines with rear drive have also achieved this and one four-wheel drive machine has managed to position all wheels under the web. Where wheels are not running down the furrow larger tyre sections can be used. One harvester uses a dual wheel assembly similar to a tandem axle trailer to achieve low ground pressure without having a too-wide tyre section.

Hydraulics have made a considerable impact on harvester design and are to be seen in the drive mechanisms for self-propelled machines as well as one unique trailed tow-row harvester from Reed & Upton which has hydraulic drive to the harvester wheels. This is said to improve traction under difficult conditions and enable a tractor with a smaller tyre width to be used.

Offset harvesters overcome the problem of the wheel in the furrow, but are limited to single-row machines. One of the most successful offset machines is a mounted harvester from Ransomes, the Faun, which is unique in having a rotating wheel and spinning vertical disc which transfers the soil and tubers to elevator webs running at right angles to the direction of work. It generally achieves a low-damage performance which is in part due to its offset configuration.

Major adjustments to the wheels are the track setting to suit different row spacing and the alignment with the tractor. It is particularly important for the wheel running in the furrow bottom or next to the ridge to be correctly set as undue pressue on the side of the ridge will cause tuber damage. Correct harvester alignment with the tractor is essential to avoid this ridge pressure from the wheels.

Long harvesters normally require larger headlands for turning and to ensure alignment with the row at the start. Steering axles on the harvester greatly increase manoeuvrability at headlands and elsewhere. Steerable rear wheels and hydraulic setting of tractor harvester alignment are invaluable aids in maintaining harvester position on sideling ground.

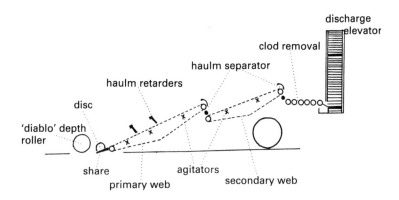

6.11 Typical unmanned elevator digger harvester—component parts

The various components of manned and unmanned harvesters have been discussed and the various adjustments outlined. To clarify the position of components on the two major types of harvester Figs. 6.11 and 6.12 have been prepared.

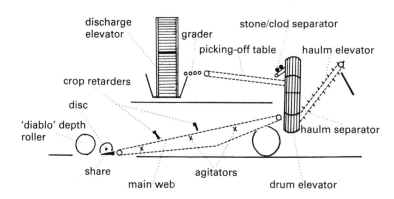

6.12 Typical manned harvester—component parts

CHOICE OF HARVESTER

There are many factors to be considered in making the choice of a potato harvester. There are the soil conditions under which it will operate, the acreage to be harvested and the harvester performance, with the overriding consideration which must be damage prevention.

Soil type
The major factor effecting choice of harvest type is the soil conditions. Unmanned Continental harvesters are really only successfully operated in conditions which ensure that almost 80 per cent of the material entering the trailer is composed of potatoes. This limits their use to lighter soils which are generally free-flowing and less likely to form clod, and to soils free from stones larger than 25 mm in diameter. Stone treatment—windrowing, removal and crushing can increase acreage suitable for the Continental unmanned harvester and is likely to lead to an increased use of unmanned harvesters in hitherto unsuitable areas. Improved pre-planting cultivation techniques which enable growers to produce a tilth relatively free of clods has further increased potential use of this harvester. Except under the most ideal conditions some

PLATE 6:5
Self-propelled Continental unmanned harvester at work

sorting of clod and stone is necessary prior to storage of the crop from this type of harvester.

The unmanned harvesters with sophisticated separation devices such as Hestair's Pacemaker harvester with X-ray separator and the Lockwood Markaire with the air-lift separator are suitable for soils which contain a high proportion of clod and stone and where labour is not available for picking-off when using a manned harvester.

Manned harvesters can be of fairly simple design, without mechanical separating methods and relying on pickers to remove most of the stone and clod. Various separation devices mentioned earlier in the chapter reduce the operator workload.

There are of course soil conditions in which it is impossible to use a complete harvester; however, some machines are more suited to heavy soil conditions than others and will work longer even in a wet season. The points to look for are a machine with a large separation area, with the main web divided to allow vigorous separation on the first section without compromising the secondary web speed. Elevators are often a problem if the separation of loose soil is not complete on the main web. Cage-type drum elevators will often block up under heavy, wet soil conditions; the flighted elevator and duplex elevator are to be preferred in this case.

It should be remembered that harvesters do not always fall clearly into the two groups, unmanned and manned. There are machines which are designed with only a limited picking-off table area. These machines can be used manned or unmanned, but the pick-off area will not always be sufficient under certain soil conditions to allow the full performance of the harvester to be used.

HARVESTER PERFORMANCE

It is unrealistic to look at harvester performance without considering the factors that might effect it. The harvesting system, its organisation, the soil type and period of operation will affect overall seasonal performance. Survey work has shown that unmanned machines are over 20 per cent faster than the equivalent sized manned machines. The cause is likely to be the pickers dictating the forward speed of the harvester. The operators will decide also the length of time each day the machine is used. Manned harvesters work fewer hours per day because the pickers are often casuals working limited hours (mothers working school hours).

Manned single-row machines have a seasonal overall rate of work of 0·1 ha/h but this may be only 65 per cent of the harvester spot rate. This emphasises how important it is to keep delay and turning times to the minimum. Spot harvesting rates range from 0·07 ha/h for a low-priced single-row machine to 0·2 ha/h for the larger, more expensive models. Unmanned two-row machines achieve a seasonal overall work rate of 0·2 ha/h, but this is often only 45 per cent of the machine type spot rate of work. Delay time due to a poorly organised bulk transport system unable to handle the increased tonnage is often the cause. A machine's seasonal performance is dependent on a combination of factors; in the UK over 200 hours of use in each year is not uncommon. The average number of working days may be only three-quarters of the main crop harvesting period of 40–50 days. A typical machine working day would be from 6·5 to 7 hours.

REDUCING DAMAGE IN THE FIELD

Potato damage will to some degree always be with us. Increased use of methods of harvesting and handling tubers which require less labour and more equipment makes the potential for damage very high.

Surveys have shown that 20 per cent of all potatoes are damaged during harvesting and handling into store, a further 10 per cent are bruised internally which makes the flesh turn blue or black. These figures will rise or fall depending on season, whether it is very dry or the conditions are good. There are producers who have damage figures far in excess of these, but there are many producers who are able to harvest and handle their potatoes with levels of surface and bruising damage considerably below the national average. It is not purely soil type, conditions or choice of equipment that cause these differences as similar farms can produce contrasting damage figures.

TABLE 6.2. PMB National Damage Survey: harvester type and damage levels

Classification	Internal bruise (per cent)	Severe damage (per cent)	Total flesh damage (per cent)	Damage index
Mean overall	12·8	8·7	23·3	137
Mean manned	14·8	9·3	24·5	145
Mean unmanned	14·4	8·0	21·4	122

It is clear that high levels of damage are often brought about by management and machine operation factors. The sources of damage can often be readily identified and the damage levels reduced significantly by simple harvester adjustment and/or modifications to the harvesting and handling system.

Soil Conditions

It is clear from observation and survey results that soil conditions contribute to the degree of damage. Dry light soils will lead to a marked increase in bruising up to 20 per cent, with flesh damage as much as 30 per cent, while peaty or clay soils would have damage only two-thirds of these levels. This is clearly a reflection of the early loss of the soil 'cushion' on the main web in dry seasons.

The percentage of stones in the soil will also affect damage levels. The type of stone is significant, angular stones causing the most flesh damage. This is where stone windrowing plays its part, drastically reducing damage levels and also increasing harvesting rate by as much as 25 per cent when unmanned harvesters can be used.

TABLE 6.3. Stones and their effect on potato damage

Stones	bruised (per cent)	Severe damage (per cent)	Total flesh damage (per cent)
Many/round	17·3	11·0	28·0
Many/angular	13·7	12·7	31·6
Negligible	13·1	7·5	20·4

TABLE 6.4. Types of damage and their causes

Type of damage	Field	Causes Harvester operation	Handling from harvester to store
Split	pressure on ridge	—	drop into trailer; drop into elevator hopper
Squash	pressure on ridge	—	discharge into elevator hopper
Slice	—	disc/share setting	—
Internal Bruise	pressure on ridge; stony or cloddy field	excessive speed of harvester webs	drop into trailer; discharge into elevator hopper
Scuff	—	excessive speed of harvester webs	—
Cuts	stony, cloddy field	excessive speed of harvester webs	projections on machinery
Holes	—	—	projections on machinery; tidying heap

Harvester preparation

The harvester must be in good mechanical order and all rubber covers and protective material must be sound. Available on the market is a resilient foam plastic (Plastazote) which does not absorb water and has good wear properties. This material can be fixed with adhesive to flat, hard areas on the machine where potatoes make contact. Areas where changes in direction take place should be examined closely, also tops of elevators where sprocket teeth can damage tubers.

The Ridge

The damage most likely to be found at this point is squashed or split tubers caused by side pressure on the ridge. Damage level may be as high as 10 per cent.

●Narrow row widths are often a major cause: consider increasing row widths to 90 cm.

●Incorrect tyre width for the row spacing. This not only applies to the harvester tractor but any previous operation such as haulm pulverising. Offset harvesters are an advantage here. Where traction is a problem with large harvesters four-wheel drive with narrower tyre widths or special dual-wheel fittings can prove the answer. Self-propelled harvesters have the large driving wheels outside the rows.

●Misalignment. It is surprising how often it is found that the harvester is not correctly aligned to the tractor and the furrow wheel is pressing on the ridge.

●Insufficient headland. Sufficient headland for turning into the rows is essential. Steering axles on some harvesters and self-propelled machines can ease this problem.

The Share

Damage at this point is often the most obvious as tubers are cut or sliced by the share due to insufficient depth. Poor depth control is often the problem with uneven planting depth and poor tilth not helping the situation. Automatic depth control or depth rollers where soils are suitable should be fitted.

Slicing can also be caused by discs at the ridge sides being poorly adjusted. Consider using the disc share. Trials have shown that this share type has a low draught requirement and that the risk of slicing is reduced.

The Main Web

This is the area where most damage occurs and where a lot can be done to reduce it. Bruising, cuts and scuffing are the most likely damage. Up to 30 per cent or more severe damage is possible.

Harvesters are designed to work under most conditions, so the separation area is large. In light soils and dry conditions soil can be lost immediately from the main web. The web should be operated at the slowest speed compatible with getting adequate separation of soil and tubers while keeping a soil cushion for almost the whole length of the web. On some light soils web speed may be at 1:1 ratio with ground speed. A digital ratio meter is available so that optimum web speed to ground speed ratio is obtained. The

PLATE 6:6
Variable speed drive for harvester web

Sovereign–Ransomes, Sims & Jefferies

ideal web speed control is independent of the tractor and fully variable from the driver's seat. This is now available on a number of harvesters.

When agitators are fitted increased web speed will give a marked increase in agitation to the web. Never agitate unless a soil cushion is present.

Under dry conditions further adjustments are available—such as main web angle and web pitch (web bar covers). The former can reduce roll-backs and the latter maintain a soil cushion.

Haulm Removers
Under certain conditions particularly where haulm is strongly attached to the tubers, the haulm can draw tubers into the rollers causing crushing and splitting. Pulverisation of desiccated haulm is worthwhile. Rollers should be kept clear of trash and properly adjusted.

Clod/Stone Separation Mechanism and Other Conveyors
It is clear from investigations that harvesters fitted with stone separation mechanisms can cause damage, particularly bruising. It is not clear, however, whether this is a factor of the conditions or the mechanism. It is important to note that a mixture of stones and potatoes will cause damage and that any subsequent handling increases it. The potential for damage is high. Greater care and constant monitoring of flesh damage and bruising are essential, particularly in dry conditions.

Separate speed control for other webs on the machine is an advantage allowing optimum running speeds, not based on pto speed. The prevention of roll-back on conveyors is important as well as maintaining the rubber covers such that impact damage is reduced. Various covers are available to give increased cushioning such as double covers and cushioned covers with air spaces.

Drops and Changes in Direction
The change from one conveyor to another is always a likely area of damage. Methods by some manufacturers have been adopted to reduce this problem, as shown in Fig. 6.13.

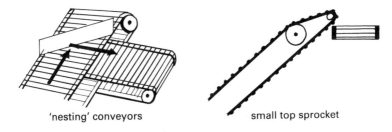

'nesting' conveyors   small top sprocket

6.13 Nesting conveyors and small top sprockets

In the case of nesting conveyors, conveyors at right angles pass through each other, and a deflector conveys tubers from one conveyor to the other. A small top sprocket can be used kept to a small diameter with a separate drive sprocket. Tubers then only have a small drop to the next conveyor. Any projections or hard surfaces should be covered with resilient foam plastic (Plastazote) and normally 13 mm is sufficient. Rubber flaps to slow the speed of tubers at change points are an advantage.

Discharge into the Trailer
Drops must be kept to the minimum. Bruising and splitting is the most likely damage at this point.
● Lower the discharge elevator as far as possible;
● Cushion the trailer floor (only part of floor may be necessary);
● Improve driver's vision by placing a grille in the front end of the trailer.
    For reduced damage on filling, the trailer should be filled from the front (this aids traction) to half its depth, and filling continued

on to the sloping face towards the rear. Top up the trailer from the rear to the front. This keeps adjustment of the discharge elevator to the minimum with only small drops.

The SIAE-designed automatic height control device for the discharge elevator can be fitted to harvesters. The cost of providing a fully cushioned trailer floor for a typical farm' trailer would be from £90 to £120 depending on trailer size.

Research has indicated the importance of sprung trailers to reduce pressure damage in transit. It is, however, unlikely that there will be a major change in the design of the agricultural trailer because of their universal uses. Suspension improvements and low-pressure tyres may be seen more in the future.

Where trailers have poor suspension drive slowly over rough ground.

POTATO DAMAGE ASSESSMENT

It is important before any damage assessment work to classify the type and degree of damage found.

The SIAE and later the PMB for their National Damage Survey in 1973 used the following classification of external visible damage:

Undamaged.

Scuffed—only skin broken, no flesh damage.

Peel—damage to flesh which can be removed by a stroke 3 mm deep of a hand potato peeler.

Severe—damage to flesh which cannot be removed by a 3 mm deep stroke of a hand peeler.

Flesh damage in the peel and particularly in the severe category may take the form of cuts, gouges, splits or crushing.

Bruising is the term applied to internal tissue damage which usually turns blue-black over a period of a few days.

The damage index was developed as a tool for comparing the performance of different machines with respect to damage and is based on the amount of peel that has to be removed from the damaged tubers. In other words it is the weight loss to the processor and consumer. The damage index can be calculated by taking a sample of 100 tubers and separating them into undamaged, scuffed, peeler and severe classes. Then the percentages are multiplied by the following factors:

Scuffed × 1
Peeler × 3
Severe × 7.

PLATE 6:7
Unmanned Continental harvester

Whitsed Victor two-row

PLATE 6:8
SIAE height control for discharge elevator to keep drop to the minimum

The total is the damage index. The index can also be expressed on a weight basis taking the weight in each class and expressing it as a percentage of the total weight of the sample. The individual classes are then multiplied by their appropriate factor.

The resultant figure should then be compared with those in Table 6.5

TABLE 6.5. Damage index

Above 300	Harvesting should stop
200–300	Very high levels of damage
130–200	Average
100–150	Fairly good
50–100	The aim

TABLE 6.6 Harvester types with typical performance range and cost

Machine type	Number of rows	Typical net* rates of work ha/h (Range)	Cost (1980)
Manned			
Trailed (medium priced) with discharge elevator	1 Row	0·05–0·16	from £5,250
Trailed (more expensive) Discharge elevator Bagger Bunker	1 Row	0·06–0·3	from £9,500 from £9,600 from £11,000
Trailed	2 Row	0·12–0·5	from £17,880
Unmanned			
Elevator digger	1 Row	0·12–0·5	from £7,000
Elevator digger	2 Row	0·15–0·5	from £11,000
Electronic separator	1 Row	0·08–0·23	from £17,500
Self-propelled	2 Row	0·25–0·75	from £32,000

* Net rate of work (ha/h) = *hectares harvesting*. Operating time—delays (h). Operating time includes turning at the headlands.

Chapter 7

HANDLING POTATOES

IT IS estimated that a single potato may travel a distance of 100 m through machinery, from the ground at harvest to being in the bag. It is essential that each operation carried out on the potato is necessary as any drop or vigorous movement is likely to cause damage.

The object of any store-filling method should be to transfer clean, soil-free potatoes into store at a rate in excess of the harvesting system with the minimal damage. It is essential that the tubers are clean and free of loose soil to allow:

● adequate and even curing temperatures for wound healing;
● successful application of fungicides;
● even and effective distribution of sprout suppressants;
● even and effective cooling of the crop.

Before examining the various handling operations which take place, it is important to discuss the factors that may affect a tuber's susceptibility to damage during these operations.

FACTORS AFFECTING TUBER SUSCEPTIBILITY TO DAMAGE

A potato, when it falls, has energy due to its mass, and velocity due to its acceleration. This energy must be dissipated on striking any surface from a given drop height and this is proportional to the mass of the tuber. The larger the potato then the greater the likelihood of damage when it falls.

The types of tuber damage can be classified as follows:

Splitting—this usually appears as one or a number of cracks radiating from the point of impact.

Crushing—when the energy of impact is spread over a small area of the tuber, due, for example, to it falling on a small narrow section of web rod then local crushing of tissue will occur.

Bruising—this occurs in layers of tissue a few millimetres under the skin and appears as a blue-black discolouration. It is possible to have a white, colourless bruise which will often dry up leaving a plug of white damaged tissue beneath the skin.

Shatter bruise—the shatter bruise is a black discoloured area with cracks normally at right-angles to splits, radiating out from the impact point. At harvest and during handling, crushing and bruising may occur without drops or impact, but this is due to situations like crushing between web rods or the pressure of wheels in the ridge sides.

Some varieties are more susceptible to damage than others, The susceptibility is affected by skin thickness, the tuber dry matter content, its shape and size, as well as the ease of detachment from the stolons. The NIAB classifies varieties for their resistance to damage as those of high or low risk to internal bruising and external damage.

Potatoes are more susceptible to damage at low temperatures. The problem can occur when putting potatoes into store during a cold, late harvest as well as when unloading the store. Tubers are more likely to bruise when cold and particularly after controlled temperature storage at 4°C. Storage methods at higher temperatures (7–9°C) will still produce tubers susceptible to bruising, but less so. Holding the potatoes for one week at 15°C prior to unloading will reduce bruising with all methods of storage when subsequent handling takes place. The minimum period for which this temperature must be maintained is not known at present.

Splitting can also be a problem with cool, very firm tubers. Raising the temperature in the store for one week will also reduce damage levels, but high temperatures may need to be avoided with some varieties, as there is some evidence that splitting can increase with temperatures in excess of 15°C. Practical considerations, therefore, often limit the store warming-up temperature to 10° Centigrade.

What is an acceptable drop height will depend on all the above factors and the surface on to which the tubers are falling. Under most conditions, damage will be avoided if the drop on to a hard surface is no more than 250 mm and on to other potatoes no more than 600 mm.

THE TRANSPORT AND UNLOADING OF POTATOES

Potatoes can be transported and emptied at the store in a number of ways. The most common in the UK is the standard agricultural trailer with a capacity from two tonne to exceeding 10 tonne. This type of trailer with rear-mounted running gear transfers a propor-

PLATE 7:1
SIAE cradle trailer for low-damage transport and emptying

tion of its weight to the rear of the tractor. Most of these trailers, if large, are fitted with tandem axles or balloon tyres and are suitable for anything but the worst conditions. Unloading is by tipping which can be fairly gentle to the tubers if the drop into the hopper can be kept to the minimum. Top-hung rear gates which can be lifted clear of the produce during tipping are an advantage. Some trailers are fitted with a front grille, so that the driver has a good vision into the trailer during filling—this is an advantage and a worthwhile conversion to existing trailers. Filling high-sided trailers can be difficult and damaging to tubers; the ability to drop one side to half its height will ease filling and reduce drops.

It is unlikely that there will be a major trend away from the general-purpose trailer for potato haulage, because of its universal use, but improved suspensions would increase speeds and reduce tuber damage. The SIAE cradle trailer was built specifically for potatoes and is fitted with a suspension system and can be emptied through its floor; the trailer operating like a clam to release the tubers and unload with little damage. Cushioned floors in standard trailers can reduce the problem of poor suspensions on rough road surfaces. The other trailer type in common use has a narrow self-unloading conveyor down its length with hopper sides to bring the tubers to the centre. Discharge can be controlled by a rising tail-gate.

There has been little use of lorry transport for potatoes from field to store in this country, certainly in parts of central and eastern England this would be possible in most harvests. On larger farms articulated lorry trailers with bulkers can be hitched to tractor-pulled bogey units, to allow passage across the field. A lorry tractor unit can then be hitched for high-speed road transport to the store. Care in filling the bulkers is necessary to avoid damage, because of their high sides.

The choice of size and number of trailers required to transport the potatoes from field to store is dependent on the harvesting rate, the distance to be travelled and the time required to unload. The larger the trailer, the more time available for travelling and unloading with a given harvesting rate; this will often allow a reduction in the number of smaller trailers required.

The transport of potatoes in boxes from the field is quite satisfactory with hand-harvesting systems, but where bulk discharge from harvesters is concerned, the difficulties of filling the boxes without tuber damage are very hard to overcome. Transferring potatoes to boxes is now almost entirely carried out at the store or farmstead after inspection and grading have taken place. Some harvesters can, however, be fitted with box carriers so that they can be filled on the harvester and then removed by rough terrain forklift.

STORE FILLING

Where potatoes have come from a manned harvester little, if any, sorting will be necessary prior to storage. However, on heavier land, stone will be dislodged from the tubers during transit. Soil extraction prior to storage is necessary to avoid cones of loose soil forming within the store which would impede ventilation. Potatoes from unmanned Continental harvesters—unless from very clod and stone-free light soils—will require soil extraction and the separation of clod and stone. Any movement of tubers will cause damage, so the organisation at this stage is important in order to keep handling to the minimum, but provide adequate sorting. Sorting facilities are dependent on the state of the crop coming into store; the choice of type, capacity and extent of the equipment required will be dependent on many factors which will be covered in the following paragraphs.

The Feed Hopper

The first item of the store-filling line is the hopper; choice of hopper will depend on the transport system and the line capacity. At its simplest, it may consist of a hopper attachment to the store elevator, wide enough to accept the full width of the trailer and

PLATE 7:2
Mobile feed hoppers of two- and three-tonne capacity

E. W. Downs and Son Ltd

fitted with a slatted base to allow some loose soil separation. The small capacity of the hopper limits turn-round time for the trailer to the capacity of the store elevator. Larger hoppers which will accept the full or part capacity of the trailer are becoming popular, as they allow more speedy turn-round of the trailers and a more constant supply of potatoes with an adjustable feed rate to suit the sorting line and conditions.

There are three basic types of feed hopper. The first is the hopper boat which has a long, preferably broad, moving floor conveyor, which is either horizontal and rising steeply at an angle to discharge, or at a slight angle throughout its length. Trailers can be tipped at the side or at the end of the hopper.

Large capacity is an advantage, supplying a reserve to the line, but often trailers can only tip part of the load and have to wait until the conveyor moves tubers away before finally emptying.

The slatted hopper is designed to be filled from the end only and has a limited capacity, normally only taking about one-third the capacity of the trailer. A broad slatted conveyor set at a steep angle feeds tubers to the line. Normally, each slat has a rubber flap, which provides the conveying surface—the tubers collecting in the depression between the slats. Over-filling of this type of hopper should be avoided as damage can be caused to the tubers

PLATE 7:3
Mobile bulk feed hopper—suitable for end filling only; note covers to protect tubers from rain

R. J. Herbert

PLATE 7:4
Slatted conveyor in bulk feed hopper

near to the slats with the increased pressure. In one type, the angle of conveyor can be altered to give a greater or lesser 'churning effect' which can be used to advantage in cleaning soil off the potatoes in sticky conditions.

The third type is the drive-in or drive-over hopper. With the drive-in hopper the feed end is left open and has track ways each side of the broad conveying web to take the wheels of the trailer.

The trailer can back up to the tubers in the hopper and tip, drawing forward to empty the trailer completely. The drive-over hoppers are similar in concept, except that the complete hopper is below ground level. The trailers must tip on to the face of the tubers to keep drop to the minimum, or a collecting canvas must be used.

With the self-unloading trailer, large hoppers are not necessary and the narrow emptying conveyor can feed directly into the store elevator or into the line. One Canadian manufacturer offers a bolt-on self-unloading conveyor unit and soil extractor that can be fitted to large tipping trailers. It is possible for more than one self-unloading trailer to be emptied at once into store.

It is important that the hopper type suits the range of trailers in use and that the drop height from the body is kept to the minimum. Hoppers with narrow discharge points should be avoided as this often leads to unnecessary churning and pressure on the tubers.

Soil Extraction

Unless tubers are coming into store very clean and soil-free, then soil extraction is necessary. There are four main types of pre-cleaner in use today.

- web
- star wheel
- spool
- coil spring.

The web type soil extractor consists of a web made up of interlocking rods, or rods fixed to side webs similar to the separating web on harvesters. The webs are normally rubber-covered and rely on the bar gap and agitation to give loose soil separation. It is unlikely that any large clod is broken up and removed with this type.

One of the most gentle soil extractors for potatoes uses the star wheel. Banks of interlocking soft rubber stars revolve on horizontal shafts set at right angles to the produce flow. The backward curved rubber fingers of the stars lift the tubers from one bank to the next, loose soil and small clod passing between the fingers. The action of the fingers which are slightly hooked, is to smash soft clod and pass it through. A rubber flap can be placed over the banks of stars and potatoes to avoid the odd potato being flicked away by the action of the fingers. Originating in Holland, this equipment is now becoming popular in the UK. Some models are adjustable for gap to suit size of material to be removed.

PLATE 7:5
Web-type soil extractor

Rekord

PLATE 7:6
Star wheel-type soil extractor

Hercules

Spools and rubber discs are used successfully as soil extractors. One machine uses a combination of rubber spools and a bank of star wheels to assist the movement of tubers along the machine. Spools and discs are not a positive conveying method and some tubers can remain on the separator for a considerable time unless a steady flow of tubers is maintained. Smearing can take place in wet conditions.

PLATE 7:7
Coil spring soil extractor

Cranford

The coil-spring soil extractor can work under a variety of conditions and relies on banks of rotating coil springs set across the direction of travel. To assist the movement of tubers the complete bed can be angled. Increased cleaning will result if the angle is reduced and the tubers retained on the springs longer.

Increased capacity of these machines is best achieved by increasing their width rather than their length, because the least agitation a crop receives with clod and stone, the least damage will be caused.

Pre-cleaners are available in a number of configurations: free-standing with soil discharge conveyor and elevators, attached to bulk hoppers with inline or right-angle delivery, and at a fixed point on a mobile sorting system.

SORTING INTO STORE

The increased use of unmanned harvesters has meant that there is a greater need for sorting of clod and stone before storage. Recently, a number of methods have been developed to ease this handling problem and reduce damage. Work at the Scottish Institute of Agricultural Engineering and on PMB surveys has highlighted that the larger the potato, the more susceptible it is to damage. Tubers over 57 mm are likely to have 75 per cent more severe damage than those within the 38–57 mm size range. These new methods have been developed to separate the larger tubers from small tubers and the clod and stone. This reduces the like-

PLATE 7:8
By-pass sizer unit which allows larger potatoes to by-pass electronic separator can also assist manual separation

E. W. Downs and Son Ltd

PLATE 7:9
Adjustable spool-type grader.

lihood of tuber damage as well as improving the efficiency of manual and static electronic sorting.

One sizer/grader can be used both into and out of store. When used into store, the potatoes pass over a soil extractor and then over a 50 mm-plus endless screen sizer. The larger tubers pass over and into store with the minimum of manual sorting. The rest pass through the screen on to the sorting conveyor, where operators pick potatoes from clod and stone, or whichever is the greater. The smaller tubers can then rejoin the large tubers into store, or they can be kept separate as desired. (H. J. Herbert Engineering.) With this system sorting can be easier with less labour.

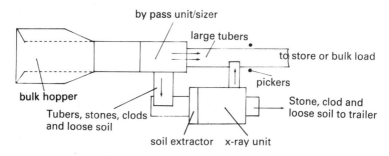

7.1 Layout of equipment with by-pass unit and electronic separator

This method of separating out the larger tubers can also be used with the static electronic sorter. The arrangement allows the large tubers to by-pass the electronic sorter, reducing the number of objects that pass in front of the X-ray eye. A by-pass unit is now available with a 50 mm-plus screen, which allows the smaller tubers, clod and stone to pass through the sizer and then separator, and rejoin the large tubers.

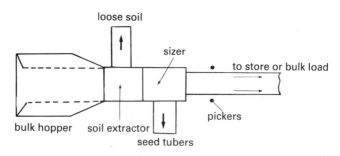

7.2 Layout of equipment for loose soil removal and seed retrieval

PLATE 7:10
X-ray static electronic separator, Marksman 150 MK2—15 tonne per hour
throughput with 50/50 crop to trash

Hestair Harvesters

PLATE 7:11
'Bystronic' separator relies on light beams to differentiate clods and stones
from tubers

E. W. Downs and Sons Ltd

PLATE 7:12
'Concertina' or 'linked' conveyors for store filling   R. J. Herbert Engineering

PLATE 7:13
Simple box filling—rubber belting strung across the box

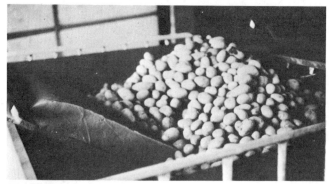

PLATE 7:14
Simple box filling—foam-covered board set at an angle within the box

Where the amount of clod or stone is small, this may be satisfactorily removed by hand off the store-filling conveyors.

It is often at this stage that removal of seed is required; an endless chain sizer can be used, or what is often preferred because of its gentle action is a spool-type sizer. The manufacturer produces a store elevator with combined spool sizer specifically for seed removel (Wytrac). Sizer types will be dealt with later in the chapter.

Static Automatic Stone/Clod Separators
The principles of the electronic and airlift separators were discussed in Chapter 6 on harvesting. These units, however, have been fully developed for static use into store or into the grading line. The Whitsed Marksman 150 and 250 automatic separator units have input capacities of 15 tonne and 25 tonne per hour respectively. Separators available from Lockwood Graders can be obtained with a variety of sorting finger spacings to suit crop grade size and achieve maximum efficiency. Recent modifications to these units have achieved a reduction in the drop necessary to enable the sensing mechanism to work; this will assist in damage reduction.

A number of new systems of separating clod and stone from potatoes have been recently introduced. One method relies on a high-intensity light source to differentiate between potato or clod/stone. An air blast keeps the lens pick-up windows clear beneath the conveyor belts. Another system which is still at the pre-production stage uses lightly-sprung fingers to separate the greater mass of the stone and clod from the potato. Considerable success has been achieved with this method. (E. W. Downs & Son Ltd). By-pass units reducing the quantity of larger tubers entering the separating mechanism would increase throughput with most of these units.

ORGANISATION INTO STORE

Store-filling 'concertina' or 'linked' conveyors allow the soil extraction and sorting facilities to be kept stationary out of the store and only the store elevator to be moved as the store is filled. Where a number of conveyors are used for store filling, it is important to keep the number and extent of the drops to the minimum. On the larger units, winching systems have been developed to pull the store elevator and linked conveyors out of the store as it is being filled.

Box Filling
Various systems have been developed for box filling to keep the

PLATE 7:15
Cascade or Zigzag box filler which can automatically be raised as the box fills

E. W. Downs and Son Ltd

PLATE 7:16
Swan neck elevator box filler

Lockwood

PLATE 7:17
Mechanical box filler

E. W. Downs and Son Ltd

drops and damage to the minimum and to provide speedy filling. At its simplest, drops into the box can be cushioned by an angled foam-covered board within the box, which can be removed as it is filled, or rubber belting strung across the box. These methods can be combined with a radius filling conveyor which pivots about one point to discharge tubers into boxes positioned at its arc of travel. Many boxes can be positioned with the conveyor moved by one man from box to box.

Box fillers are of many types: there is the angled box filler where the box is angled to a horizontal feed conveyor, as the box fills the box returns to the horizontal, keeping the drop to the minimum. The cascade, or zig-zag, consists of a number of pockets of heavy canvas which transfer in small steps the tubers to the bottom of the box. As the box fills, a probe 'concertinas' the cascade pockets. These two types can be arranged in pairs, the feed conveyor being fed from the line at the centre and the direction of the tuber flows to left or right being controlled by a probe switch operated by the full box. This achieves continuous filling with adequate time for box changeover. More expensive are the elevator box fillers. Having a swan neck they can reach to the bottom of the box; a probe raises the discharge elevator as the box fills. When the box is full the flow of tubers is stopped and the elevator either swings over to a second box, or a turntable presents another empty box under the elevator.

A mechanical box filler developed recently by E. W. Downs relies on the increased weight of the box as it fills to lift from the box a curved foam-covered chute which cushions the tuber drop.

Store Elevators

Bulk elevators can be considered under three headings:
- conventional store elevators with or without swinging head;
- telescopic centre pivot elevators;
- swinging boom elevators.

One of the major factors that must be considered before store elevator purchase is the way in which the elevator operates. It is essential that loose soil does not form cones under a stationary elevator discharge, as this will impede ventilation of the stack and seriously affect the efficiency of sprout suppressants. The elevator type and size for a particular store will depend on the rate of filling required, the stack height and width, and the labour available.

The standard conventional elevator uses almost universally the moulded cleated conveyor belt with closely-spaced cleats to reduce roll-back. Most have a troughed or concave belt to allow alternative crops, such as grain, to be elevated. At their simplest, the elevators consist of a single angled elevator bed which is adjustable for height and fitted with wheels which can be swivelled to allow the elevator to swing from side to side, so that the discharge point can be altered regularly. The next stage is an adaptation for root crops: a swinging head is fitted. This is a small section of horizontal conveyor fitted at the top of the elevator, which swings automatically from side to side over an arc of 3 m or so. This reduces the risk of soil coning. Elevator reach is important for a particular store height. Adequate elevator length is necessary to allow sufficient room for the angle of repose of the stack. For every 1 metre of stack height, allow at least 1·5 m of clear elevator reach.

Some elevators are fitted with a 'luffing' head which enables the top 1–1·5 m of the elevator top to be angled downwards to reduce discharge drop and to avoid spillage. In combination with the swinging head, this allows gentle placement of the crop into store and into bulkers.

Telescopic centre pivot elevators have been designed so that the complete elevator boom can swing from one side of the store to the other. This gives an even distribution of tubers. This is carried out automatically, the extent of the swing being adjusted by, for

PLATE 7:18
Store filling elevator

PLATE 7:19
Swinging boom elevator for large stores, will slew a width of up to 14·6 metres

Fyson Barnstormer

example, pegs which can be positioned to give the desired swing from the operating mechanism. Not only does the elevator swing, but it can also be made to telescope. Thus the discharge point can be moved forward as the stack is made up. This facility can be used to good advantage when filling, by adopting a 'terraced filling' technique. Normally, stores are filled to the full height with the elevator discharging on to the top of the bulk face with subsequent avalanching or roll-back of tubers, which can lead to damage. If the store is filled in two stages to a depth of, say, 1·5 m on the first section covered by the elevator, then raising and extending the boom to fill the remainder, this can reduce the undesired roll-back.

Some of this type also incorporate an endless-chain soil extractor, although collecting the soil can be difficult. An additional small elevator is necessary to supply the centre pivot elevators as the feed-on point is at high level (1·5–3 m) depending on model.

Swinging boom elevators are used in large stores and can fill a store width of anything up to 15 m from one position. They normally have a good reach and are fully adjustable for discharge height. The swing can be controlled automatically like the pivot elevator and they are not normally telescopic. Very high rates of store filling are possible with these machines: up to 120 t per hour. Some models include soil extractor sections.

There are a number of fully automatic store filling systems. One system, which is worthy of note, uses a gantry which covers the width of the store and travels the length of the building. Tubers are fed into the store at the middle, on to a conveyor which runs for about half the store length at high level and which is fixed and moves with the gantry. Tubers are ploughed off on to an angled conveyor with flights which discharges on to a horizontal conveyor which is raised and lowered on a parallelogram linkage. This lower conveyor can operate in either direction and, being only half the width of the store, can therefore discharge over the whole width. One advantage of this conveying system is that the store can be layer-filled, thus avoiding all the problems of roll-back and avalanching down the stack face. The complete system can operate automatically, probes operating the movement and height of the lower conveyor.

Box Handling into Store

Handling boxes into store involves the use of a forklift. Rough terrain or industrial forklifts can be used. The rough terrain forklift takes a lot of room and is difficult to manoeuvre in a small area.

PLATE 7:20
Conveyor type store unloader

A typical machine takes a length of at least 5 m to position opposite a box. Side shift will help position the boxes tightly into store. The industrial truck is more flexible and can be virtually turned in its own length, however it is limited to level hard surfaces, because of its small wheels. Retracted mast height is important if access through low doors is required. Storage of boxes can be as high as 8·5 metres to make maximum use of the space available.

STORE EMPTYING

Unloading the store and the subsequent handling operation after harvesting are the next major sources of potato damage. As mentioned earlier in the chapter, potatoes are often cold and may be turgid when leaving store and very susceptible to damage. Care is therefore essential with this operation. In the UK the majority of potatoes are handled out of store by hand and fork, or by the bulk potato bucket. In 1971 the PMB showed that hand forking caused 13 per cent severe damage whereas with a bucket the damage level was 6–9 per cent.

The larger the bucket, the greater the reduction in damage due to less contact of the sides and leading edge of the bucket. Bucket capacities of up to 3 tonne are now possible on industrial loaders. The bucket design and its use are important. The bucket should be wider than the tractor track, clear of internal obstruction and divisions, have a rounded back with side cheeks sloping at an angle of 30°, the edges being rounded. Slow, gentle operation with a light tractor is crucial. Hydraulic controlled tipping of the bucket is essential.

Apart from the standard agricultural tractor with hydraulic bucket on the fore-end loader, there are the rough terrain forklifts with large capacity root buckets and the highly manoeuvrable skid loaders (Bobcat) which have gained in popularity over the last few years. Forklifts which allow quick and speedy interchange of attachments from buckets to forks and to bale handling units are becoming a necessity on the larger arable farm.

The Dutch self-propelled store unloader can be operated to produce little damage, but its use does require a series of horizontal conveyors to transport the potatoes from the unloader to the grading line or bulker elevator. The unloader consists of a shallow angled conveyor mounted on a wheeled powered chassis. The front throat of the conveyor is fitted with a share type blade which runs at ground level and feeds tubers on to the conveyor. At the rear of the unit the potatoes feed on to a conveyor which is free to pivot. An operator normally sits on the machine and guides it into the stack.

Conveying with water or fluming is an excellent way of moving tubers out of store, but it is essential that the potatoes are then washed and processed or packed immediately for sale. Normally, this technique is operated at stores, connected with a washing and pre-packing plant, or as an unloading method at processing factories as it provides a valuable part of the washing cycle.

Filling Bulkers

A range of equipment is available to fill bulkers at a high rate and yet keep drops to the minimum, but unfortunately they seldom are used. The most common method is the standard store elevator, but unless a suitable padded area or mattress is used at the initial filling point, tuber damage can be serious. A 'zig-zag cascade' unit

PLATE 7:21
Filling a bulker with an
elevator and cascade
unit

E. W. Downs and Son Ltd

can be fitted to the top of a standard elevator, but make sure the elevator is suitably weighted to take the additional weight of the cascade full of tubers. For the larger farm or co-operative a drop-neck elevator with automatic height control should be used.

In the USA the lorry bulkers are filled from the rear, using long telescopic fillers entering from the tail-board end and filling from front to back onto the sloping face of the tubers.

Specialist handling engineers have developed sophisticated filling equipment which will feed tubers from high-level bulk hoppers on to a flighted conveyor which is able to run the full length of the bulker, the tubers falling no greater distance than 225 mm and filling at any level.

Chapter 8

PREPARATION FOR MARKET

THE CHOICE of available equipment for potato grading is wide and will depend on many factors: the throughput required per hour; market requirements; soil type; labour and when it is available, and the storage system. The operations of grading can be classified under four main headings, as follows.

1. Removal of foreign matter—clod, stone, and loose soil.

2. Inspection and removal of substandard tubers: for example tubers which are diseased or affected by rots, damaged to a depth greater than 3 mm, affected by greening, damaged by pests or frost, misshapen or affected by growth cracks, secondary growth or Hollow Heart; and also tubers which are discoloured internally or bruised, are tainted or affected by growth shoots. Some tolerance of faults may be allowed, for example to 5 per cent by weight or 1·25 kg in 25 kg. Faults can not always be seen by the inspector and selective sampling may be necessary.

3. Sizing: marketing regulations will set minimum size grades and often a maximum size grade. For example, the packed sample should not contain tubers above 80 mm riddle or below the 40 mm riddle, and longer than 165 mm. Processors and pre-packers may be stricter in their requirements.

4. Weighing and packaging: potatoes may leave the farm in bulk to the processor and pre-packer, or for example, in 25 kg multi-walled paper sacks.

Other operations, such as washing, brushing and peeling, may be carried out, depending on the outlet.

FEEDING THE LINE

The different types of feed hopper were discussed in the section dealing with handling into store. The requirements for feeding potatoes into the grading line are slightly different, however. The object is to provide a continuous supply of tubers to the line at a rate that can be readily adjusted to suit the optimum conditions for sorting and sizing; and to form a reserve of tubers so that the line can still be operated with an intermittent supply from the

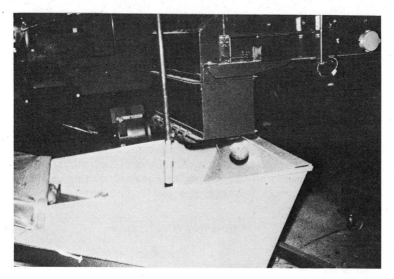

PLATE 8:1
Probe within elevator hopper controls feed rate of tubers through the line

store. The usual capacity of a bulk hopper is about 4 tonne, although sizes ranging from 2·5 tonne to 10 tonne or more are available. The rate of feed is normally controlled by a variable speed motor that can be readily adjusted by a simple dial type control. Probe sensing is also available which will control a fixed speed motor, the grading line having variable flow rate control on, for example, the feed elevator.

The bulk hopper will be filled by various means, the most common being the bulk bucket mounted on a fore-end loader, forklift or industrial loader. This can be carried out gently if fitted with hydraulically controlled tipping. Potato storage boxes can be tipped by a forklift attachment or separate box tippler. There are two main types of forklift-mounted box tipplers: the 'rotary head' and the 'forward tippler'. The rotary head tips to the side, the box pivoting about its centre. This does make it difficult to avoid a large drop for the potatoes as the box must be raised well above the heap or hopper to allow it to pivot. The box should have retaining slats at the base of the forklift entry points. The forward tipping attachment tips the box about its front edge: this makes it easier to tip into a hopper or on to a heap of tubers without a large drop. An adjustable box retainer resting on the front edge of the box holds the box in place as it tips.

The separate box tipplers are self-contained units which can be positioned over the bulk hopper; discharge height can be adjusted to suit the hopper. The box is placed within a framework which is tipped hydraulically, or with direct electric motor drive. A less expensive model can be tipped by using the fork lift.

The next major item on the grading line is a soil extractor or pre-cleaner. The mechanisms will be similar to those used into store, but because of the lower throughput of the grading line, they need not be so large unless they are also used into store.

Suitable chutes and conveyors for removal of the spoil are necessary—trailers or boxes being suitable containers.

INSPECTION

The position of the inspection table is important for efficiency of sorting. Unless there is a pre-grader to take out smaller tubers the best position for the table is after the grader. In certain situations where a pre-grader is used and there are to be a number of grade sizes, the whole crop prior to grading should be inspected as this tends to be more efficient in labour usage.

There are two main types of inspection table: the roller, and belt. The roller table consists of a series of wooden or plastic-covered rollers which both roll and convey the potatoes so that the whole potato can be inspected. The rollers are turned either by a friction pad, or by the more positive rack and pinion on the roller. It is normal for the table to run up at a slight angle as this encourages the tubers to turn and spread out over the table. Flat belts can be used, but some method of turning the tubers is necessary. A rubber flap placed across the table can ensure sufficient turning of the tubers. Potatoes from some soils may carry the dirt with them—this can lead to clogging of the rollers. In these situations a flat-belt inspection table or pre-cleaner may be necessary.

There are many factors that will contribute to the efficiency of manual inspection. Work by the Potato Marketing Board, Scottish Institute of Agricultural Engineering and in America has highlighted some of these. The speed of the tubers past the operators should be adjustable, preferably steplessly. The number of potatoes passing in front of each operator appears to be more important than the level of defects. For highest throughput 250–300 tubers/minute/operator, or about 1·5–1·8 t/h (Malcolm *et al.*, 1952) is recommended. The PMB uses a figure per person of 0·72 t/h for low throughputs, 1·44 t/h medium and 2·16 t/h for high throughputs. The level of manning must depend on the outlet and to a certain extent the state of the crop.

Most efficient inspection seems to occur at a conveyor speed of 6–9 m/minute and a rotational speed of the rollers which gives 1·5–2 revolutions of the potato in a distance of 0·3 metres.

Lighting is most important. In the USA an intensity of 150 lx at the surface of the rollers from fluorescent tubes is recommended. 'Northlite' or 'Kolourite' tubes appear to give the best results.

The number of persons grading and their position does affect their efficiency. Having operators opposite each other allows more defective potatoes to be seen. It appears that most people prefer to have the potatoes moving from right to left and to be angled at 45° so that the oncoming tubers are seen for a longer time.

The operators should not have to stretch more than 450 mm when standing at the side of the table. They can then easily pick off rejects and place them down a front or side chute, or on to a central conveyor for subsequent disposal.

Semi-Automatic Inspection Aids

Electronics can assist in the removal of defective material; two systems of assisting the inspection have been evolved. If one can take the burden of actually removing the damaged or green tubers away and leaving inspection to a decision-making process with a minimum of manual movement, the speed and efficiency of inspection can be improved. The SIAE designed machine uses a wand to touch and reject the selected tuber. A Lockwood device uses a pendulum which the operator has to swing to home a light beam on to the 'damaged' tuber and then pull a trigger to reject it. A more advanced Lockwood device—'Teleselect'—has a TV screen on which a colour image of the potatoes passes; the operator employs an electronic pointer to select the tuber to be rejected on the screen. This device certainly keeps the hand movement to the minimum, but may lose some accuracy of selection due to TV screen presentation.

The SIAE separator uses a roller table with moulded rollers so that the potatoes settle in four lanes, each in individual cells. As on a roller table the tubers rotate. The defective potato is then touched by the wand and is rejected at the end by a high-speed plunger. The wand emits a radio frequency, on touching the potato this is picked up by a matrix of coils under the rollers. The signal is then transferred from the matrix to the appropriate plunger to reject the tuber.

These inspection aids can improve the quality of inspection or

PLATE 8:2
Electronic selection mechanism with pendulum held light beam

Lockwood

PLATE 8:3
Loctronic Teleselect—the operator isolates the object to be rejected on a TV monitor for automatic rejection by pneumatic fingers

PLATE 8:4
SIAE semi-automatic inspection table showing operator with hand-held wands

increase throughput at similar efficiencies to manual sorting. Throughputs at similar efficiencies to manual sorting can be increased threefold with electronic inspection aids. Improved working conditions and reduced operator fatigue will also result.

Under development in the USA and United Kingdom are inspection devices which examine electronically the inside of the tuber so that tubers with hollow heart or internal discolouration due to bruising or disease can be rejected.

SIZERS

There are three main types of size graders:
1. Endless screen
2. Reciprocating riddle
3. Spool.

The endless screen sizer consists of a flexible mesh screen which normally passes around two pintle rubber-covered rollers. A third plain roller positioned beneath the other two draws the screen down to provide a space for the cross-conveyor. The screen is gently agitated at its centre by eccentric idlers which assist the passage of the tubers through the screen. A series of these sizers

PLATE 8:5
Mobile grading unit using endless screen sizers, web-type soil extractor and roller inspection table with a capacity of 5 tonne per hour

PLATE 8:6
'Stacked' reciprocating riddle sizer

can be put together to give a range of grades. Each unit runs at a slight angle to feed on to the next and to retain the tubers on the screen long enough to be sorted. Width of screen determines its throughput rather than speed. For example, a 600 mm screen can deliver about 5 tonne per hour and a 900 mm screen about 10 tonne per hour. The grades are delivered at right angles to the line, the over-sized tubers being delivered at the end. On some units a roller inspection table conveyor can collect the tubers direct from the screen. Drive to the sizer is often single speed, but variable speed is an advantage.

The reciprocating riddle sizer is available in a number of forms. There is the stacked riddle, where the riddles are arranged according to size, one above the other, the large mesh riddle being uppermost. This can be said to have one major advantage and that is that the largest tuber travels the least distance—this keeps damage to the minimum. It does allow as well a large number of grades to be sized within a small area. A combing device, or bar, passes periodically between and beneath each riddle to dislodge any tubers caught in the mesh.

Using a similar mesh, but reciprocating in a different manner, is the jump grader. Here the screen lifts as well as reciprocates, passing the tubers along in a series of steps. The screens for different sizes are placed one after another, the smallest first, the large tubers travelling the full length of the unit. In both types the riddles are available as plastic-covered metal or as rubber-covered plywood, or steel, with various sized holes.

The spool-type sorter has spools arranged side by side on a series of shafts which rotate in the same direction. The apertures can be varied by either selecting different spools or by adjusting the spacing between spool shafts by a screw mechanism. Sizing is normally quite accurate and when the potatoes are dry there is the additional benefit of a cleaning action, but wet and diseased tubers can cause smearing.

Changing the riddle size on the endless screen sizers is more difficult and the screens more expensive than the reciprocating riddle.

There are a number of other graders which are suitable for potatoes. One worthy of note is the expanding pitch roller grader. To look at, it is similar to a roller table but as the rollers convey the tubers along, the gap between them increases, sizing the tubers. The machine is gentle in action and infinitely adjustable for roller gap. The mechanism is, however, fairly complicated and expensive to purchase.

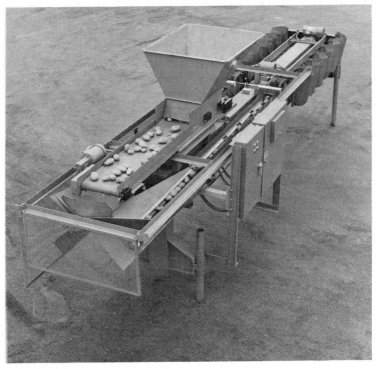

PLATE 8:7
Electronic sizer grades up to four precise grades at up to 9 tonne per hour
E. J. Tong

Electronics in Sizing

In the next few years there is likely to be a considerable increase in the use of electronics for sizing. The Optosizer (Loctronic) uses a special camera which scans the potatoes and thus determines their size. A micro-computer which registers the size operates the air-cushioned fingers which transfer the potatoes gently to the appropriate conveyor. Three size grades are possible at a capacity of up to 15 tonne per hour. An American machine introduced into the UK by E. J. Tong will automatically grade up to six sizes at 9 tonne per hour, that is four precise grades plus under- and over-sized. The tubers are carried on a series of four polyurethene belts, each progressively getting faster towards the scanning head. As each potato passes through the light matrix, the machine computes its size and volume and passes the signal to one of six fibre-glass blades, which then divert the tubers to the appropriate outlet. A simple plug-in board allows the size grades to be adjusted in 7 gramme increments in the 156–454 gramme range.

PLATE 8:8
Mechanical in-bag weighing machine for 25 kg bags

E. J. Tong

The major advantage of electronic sizing is to reduce the amount of movement and damage the tubers receive with normal grading methods.

WEIGHING AND PACKAGING

The next stage after sizing and inspection is weighing and bagging. In the UK most potatoes leave the farm in 25 kg paper bags which are closed either by stitching or by wire ties. One problem with weighing machines is meeting the Department of Trade and Industry standards for automatic weighing. The current regulations state that the machine must not underweigh or overweigh by more than a 125 gramme maximum. This is difficult to achieve with the range of potato sizes. If the weigher cannot reach this standard check-weighing must take place. The simpler, less expensive automatic weighing machines do not have a topping-up mechanism, therefore on reaching the desired weight the tuber feed is immediately switched to the next bag. Some under- or over-weighing will occur so check-weighing will be required. The unit has two bag holders, the bags being filled alternately, allowing an almost continuous feed. Weighers of this type can weigh typically up to 5 tonne per hour or two hundred 25 kg bags per hour, and would require at least two operators, one on the bagger, another stitching or wire tying. Further assistance would be required for stacking on the pallet.

The fully automatic weigher eliminates the need for topping up by the operator. Two belts, each flighted, feed from the weigher hopper into the bag; the larger of the two belts fills the bag to within 400–500 gramme of the correct weight. It then stops and the smaller trickle feed belt continues to feed one tuber at a time until the correct weight is achieved. The mechanism then switches the feed to the empty bag. Some bagger units have an intermediate hopper in which the product is weighed; this should, however, be kept clear of a build-up of soil or variations in weight will occur.

The automatic bagging and weighing systems have been developed to a stage where the operator merely needs to place the bag on the feed position where it is automatically held by a clamp. The Walthamatic 600 model weigher bagger has a four-position head; after the bag is clamped the head indexes through 90° where the bag is filled from the bulk elevator to just under the weight required. The bag, still clamped, moves another 90° to a check-weight position. This is fed by a narrow elevator which tops up to the exact weight. The bag is then deposited on the conveyor for wire tying or stitching. A unit of this type can deal with up to 600 bags per hour or 15 tonne per hour. This unit would require one person on the weigher, one on the bag-closer and another stacking the bags on pallets. There are now baggers that supply the bags automatically to the weighers, and also units that can bag and weigh from a roll of net or polythene, the bag being automatically sealed or stitched.

Bag closing of paper sacks is by manual or automatic wire tiers. The automatic wire-tying machines are normally column mounted over a bag conveyor, the height being adjustable to suit bag size, although choice of model will depend on the range of bag sizes. The output of these machines can be very high, closing in the region of 1,300 bags per hour so they can serve the supply from two or more weighers. An operator is often needed to guide the bags into the jaws of the machine, although automatic feeding is possible with suitable guides on the unit.

PLATE 8:9
Automatic weighing and prepacking machine for dry brushed or washed tubers in weights up to 7 kg

Metromethods Ltd

Stitchers are available in two forms, the fixed or column-mounted stitcher and the portable unit. The fixed machines are normally mounted over a conveyor and column-mounted to be adjusted for height. An operator is often required to align the bag and to operate the stitcher. A typical sewing speed is around 11–15 m per minute, which may give up to 900 bags per hour depending on feed rate. The portable units are normally supported from above on a negative gravity hoist and this allows the operator easily to position the unit for height and it will hang clear of the bagging area when not in use. A typical capacity would be 5–8 seconds/bag.

Weighing and bagging for pre-packing is a very large subject and there are many systems to choose from. Choice of bag is often made by the supermarket or market outlet and will normally fit within the 2–6 kg range, the bags in the UK normally being of polythene with breather holes and sealed with clips or tape. Fully automatic machines are available which weigh potatoes into wicketed bags (that is bags with a tongue or flap which allows automatic filling). Becoming more popular are the fully automatic machines which make up the bag from the roll, sealing the polythene down the length to form a tube, the weighed potatoes being fed into the tube before it is sealed. The tube is then sealed at both ends by a unit that seals the top of one bag and the bottom of the next as well as cutting it. The bagger also positions the motif, etc., centrally on the packet.

There are automatic pallet stackers for materials like fertiliser, but the handling of potatoes must be particularly gentle. Three-sided pallet formers will assist with making a square stack. A pallet turntable will reduce the amount of walking required in making the stack.

Brushers and Washers for Potatoes

In some situations where tuber appearance is spoilt by soil or even sprout suppressant dust on the surface, brushing will produce a better-looking sample without going to the extent of washing. Brushers are of various types. They can consist of a conveyor over which are a number of spinning shafts, each fitted with strands of canvas fabric or soft bristle brush to form a fairly gentle rubbing action, or the potatoes pass over a series of rotating brush-covered shafts either across or with the direction of travel.

Where potatoes are required for pre-packing, washing is often required. Fluming from the store provides a means of pre-soaking the tubers and making washing easier; however this is not always possible and full reliance must be placed on the washer. The most popular type is the immersed barrel washer. The rotating wire mesh or wood-slat barrels are partly immersed in a tank of water, the roots being tumbled repeatedly by the rotation of the barrels. Pintle rubber and brush linings to the barrels can be used to increase the scrubbing action. The process of feeding in the potatoes, the angle of the barrel and angled flights within the barrel combine to move the tubers through the barrel and on to the slatted elevator. A fresh-water rinse is applied from overhead sprays at this point, this additional water filling the barrel tank with the displaced water going to waste. Machines of this type (Pylbro by P. J. Edmunds and the Barrett washer) would use 180–270 l of water for each tonne of potatoes.

Adequate drainage must be allowed before the tubers enter the bag. Surplus moisture can be removed by sponge roller driers. These units consist of a bank of rollers covered with absorbent sponge rubber over which the tubers pass: a squeezing system removes surplus water from the sponges.

Peeling

This is more a factory rather than farm process, although some farm organisations carry it out. There are three methods available. The least expensive is the abrasive peeler where the tubers are 'rumbled' about in a carborundum-lined barrel for a period of time. A constant flow of water removes the residue from the barrel. The machines usually operate on a batch basis. Lye-peeling uses a weak caustic soda solution to remove the skin, washing with water cleans off the caustic soda and pulpy peel left on the tuber. Steam-peeling is the next method which subjects the tubers to a high temperature within a pressure vessel. It is only the outer skin that requires cooking and once the pressure is released, the outer layers can be washed away with water. Rapid release of the pressure can cause flash steaming on the surface of the tubers assisting with skin removal. The effluent from these processes is very strong because of its considerable starch content leading to high biological oxygen demand (B.O.D.) Sophisticated effluent disposal methods are often required.

LAYOUT OF GRADING LINES

When designing a grading line layout one should if possible try and divide it into three sections: cool and dirty; warm and clean; and cool for pre-market storage.

In the first section are the intake facilities, the dump or feed hopper and the soil extractor. Soil from the pre-cleaner should be preferably conveyed outside the building into boxes or trailers. Most people are present in the next section: inspection, sizing and weighing, and bagging. This must be kept fairly warm for the operators. It is, however, not necessary to keep the whole section at the same temperature. The persons on the inspection area are stationary and will require the warmest conditions. Enclosing this section within a light structure can retain the warmth, reduce noise and allow reasonable conversation or the use of radios. Heating should be by warm air at foot level. The operators in other areas (the weigher and bagger units) are more active. Mobile heaters can be used at these points.

Sub-standard potatoes removed at inspection can be conveyed to boxes for subsequent disposal. Boxes can be used to collect other grades, oversize, mids or chats for subsequent weighing and bagging where necessary.

The storage and dispatch area must be kept cool and dry, but must be frost-free.

PLATE 8:10
Grading line design—broad full-width elevator keeps speed of tubers low and allows even feeding of line components

Grading Line Example
A typical grading line for the large farm or co-operative. To have a throughput of 15 t/h to cope with high rates required during certain periods. The average tonnage per day would be 60 tonne. The line operating during non-peak periods for 4–6 hours each working day.

Typical labour requirement:
1   Grading line manager or farmer
1   Secretary (part time)
1   Forklift driver
8+ Casual/regular pickers (depending on sample)
3–4 Main weigher/baggers including pallet stacking
2   Additional small weighing and bagging unit for oversize or mids.
Up to 12–13 persons could be casual staff.

Grading machinery—typical 15 tonne/hour line:

	£
Dump hopper with speed control, *e.g.*, six tonne capacity	4,500
Box tipper (standing over dump hopper)	1,560

PLATE 8:11
Keep tuber drops to the minimum—cushion drops where they occur

PLATE 8:12
Multi-grader—complete mobile grading unit which can be used into and out
of store

R. J. Herbert Engineering

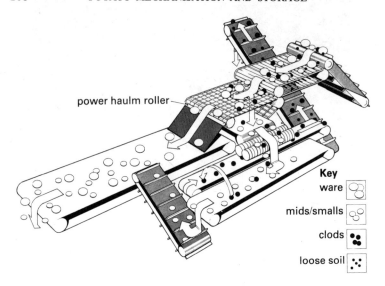

power haulm roller

Key

ware

mids/smalls

clods

loose soil

8.1 Multi-grader—suitable for pre-cleaning/grading into or out of store
Crop-flow diagram by courtesy of R. J. Herbert (Engineering)

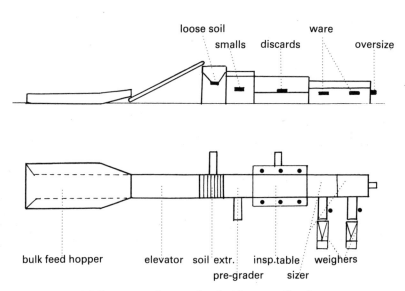

loose soil

smalls   discards   ware   oversize

bulk feed hopper   elevator   soil extr.   insp.table   weighers
pre-grader   sizer

8.2 Component layout of typical large grading line

Sizing and grading system including:
elevator
soil extractor
roller inspection table
two sizing riddle units
various size conveyors 12,000
Box filler—for oversize, etc. 600
Conveyor and elevators for waste, etc. 1,600
Weighers—there are a number of alternatives, for example:
1. Automatic machinery complete with
   ancillary equipment
   wire tying—three persons $\left.\rule{0mm}{10mm}\right\}$ 12,500
   stitching—four persons

   or:
2. Two smaller machines requiring an extra man .... (7,000)
   Small additional weigher for other grades 3,000
   TOTAL line cost at 1980 prices 35,760

Extra items would include:
Additional electrical work, heating and operator staging. Cost of laying on mains electricity supply will depend on site.
Building: a new insulated building 23 m long and 14 m wide with doors at each end, toilet facilities and rest room and concrete apron.

Gross cost: £30,000

A building of this size would provide adequate buffer storage for 50 tonne in boxes as well as dispatch storage on pallets. Pallet racking for storage of bagged potatoes will save a lot of space.

References
MALCOM, D. G., DEGARMER, P. E., 'Visual Inspection of Products for Surface Characteristics in Grading Operations', *USDA Production and Marketing Administration MRR 45*, 1952.

Chapter 9

POTATO STORAGE (1)—
VENTILATION

THE POTATO TUBER

THE POTATO tuber is a living organism containing about 75–80 per cent water. It has a cork-like skin with small pores which allows evaporation and respiration to occur.[1]

The potato tuber can potentially be stored for several months with eventual termination by sprout growth, wilting and changes in composition, such as sweetening which accompanies senescence.[2] In practice, losses in storage can be unnecessarily high; on a survey in 1961–2 of forty-one farms in Great Britain the average rotting was shown to be 15 per cent (range 2–68 per cent).[3] Although approximately twenty years has passed since this survey, there has not been a marked improvement in potato storage.

Therefore, when storing potatoes, there are two main objectives: one is to prolong the storage life of the potato as an organism and the second is to retain its quality as a food. Unfortunately, these do not require the same environmental conditions as potatoes store for a very long time at around 2°C, but they then become sweet and not acceptable; therefore a compromise has to be reached.

Summarising: the humidity should be kept high to avoid wilting and the temperature should be kept high enough to avoid sweetening and low enough to cut down the possibility of disease and sprouting.

CHARACTERISTICS OF POTATOES

Before going further in considering potato storage, a list of the physical characteristics of potatoes may be useful. Most of these characteristics will be referred to again later.

Rate of water loss
    0·17 per cent/week per mb water Vapour Pressure Deficit.[4]

In first week water loss possibly four times as much. Every 1 per cent by weight of sprouts increases potential loss by 0·08 per cent/week/mb/VPD.

Environmental limits
Freezing point −1°C to −2°C.
Internal breakdown 35°C+.
Safe limits 0°C to 20°C.

Rate of respiration

0°C	18 Watts/tonne	
5°C	9 Watts/tonne	Typical figures
10°C	12 Watts/tonne	for ware and
15°C	15 Watts/tonne	process potatoes.

Loading depth
3 m to 4·5 m.

Bulk density
1·5 m³/t (667 kg/m³).

Angle of repose
30°–40° (normally considered 35°).

Sugar content

0°C	4–5%	
2°C	1·5–2%	
4°C	1–1·5%	Typical figures
6°C	0·5–0·8%	for medium-term storage.
8°C	0·3–0·5%	
10°C	0·2–0·3%	

Thermodynamic properties
Specific heat 3·6 kJ/kg/°C.
Thermal conductivity 58 W/m/°C of tuber flesh.
Potential heat transfer to air at 0·2 m/s (proportional to $V^{0.31}$).[5]
In practice the heat transfer is limited by the heat capacity of the air involved.

Resistance to airflow

$P = KV^{1.8}$ where P = pressure in mm water gauge per metre depth.

V = approach velocity in m/h.

K = 5.3×10^{-5} for clean potatoes.
or 7.7×10^{-4} for potatoes with 20% earth.

(Sprouting potatoes can increase the resistance by up to a factor of four.)

Recommended storage temperatures

Ware (long term)	4–5°C
Ware (short term)	5–8°C
Processing (long term)	7–8°C
Processing (short term)	10°C.

VENTILATION EQUIPMENT

As mentioned previously, potatoes respire, giving off heat, moisture and carbon dioxide and if they are to be stored satisfactorily these must be removed and the rate of respiration restrained. The way in which this is done is by passing air through the stack of potatoes either by using natural convection currents or by using a fan (forced ventilation). Before looking at the different types of potato store, it is useful to consider the different pieces of ventilation equipment.

Types of Fan

If forced ventilation is required for the potatoes a decision must be made on the type of fan. As mentioned in the chapter on potato sprouting, when quoting the performance of a fan it is important to give the volume it transmits and the pressure against which it is working.

Propeller fan—this type is used for moving large volumes of air at low pressure (up to 5 mm of water) which is of little use in potato storage except for moving air around a box store.

Aerofoil axial fan—this type normally has more than four blades of aerofoil cross section and the air does not change direction on going through the fan. The maximum pressure against which this type of fan can work depends on the angle of the blades (pitch angle) to the airstream, but these fans can be made to work efficiently (75 per cent) against the typical pressure produced in a potato store of 50 mm of water. These fans can be noisy and in some cases a silencer is needed which reduces performances slightly.

Centrifugal fan—this type of fan brings the air in at the centre and pushes it out at the edge in a direction at right angles to the incoming air. The centrifugal fans used in agriculture have backward curved blades and are capable of working against pressures of 100–200 mm of water. These fans are not as efficient as axial aerofoil fans, partly because the air has to go through a right angle.

Paddle blade fan—a straight-bladed form of centrifugal fan now

PLATE 9:1
Propeller fan

Myson

PLATE 9:2
Axial fan,
shown with
electric
heater bank

Myson

PLATE 9:3
Centrifugal fan

Ventec Agricultural Ltd

PLATE 9:4
Stacked axial fans

Myson

rarely used. It suffers from the disadvantage that it will, if inadvertently operated against little or no back pressure, 'overload', or move such large volumes of air that the driving motor is overloaded and damaged.

In most cases an aerofoil axial fan is used for potato storage as it is the cheapest type of fan per volume of air moved against 50 mm of water. Also, as the aerofoil axial fan is more efficient than the centrifugal fan, there is less heat given to each unit volume air, which is clearly important when the intention is to cool the crop. The typical rise in temperature of air passing through an aerofoil axial fan is less than 1°C.

If possible, two smaller aerofoil axials should be used rather than a single larger one for the following reasons:

1. The electrical starting load will be considerably less with two smaller fans starting one after another than with one large fan (any control system should ensure that the two fans do not come on together).
2. When recirculation is available it does not require a ventilation rate as high as if air was being used to cool the crop, so if two fans are available, one only need be used for recirculation, saving on the running costs.
3. If a store is being unloaded over a period of time, it may be necessary to ventilate with cold air when the store is only partly full, again only one fan is needed. In fact, two fans on only a small part of the store could cause no more cooling than one and in extreme cases desiccation could occur.

The main reason against using two smaller fans rather than one big one is the higher capital cost, although this is not always the case.

It can be worthwhile installing a straightener just downstream of an aerofoil axial fan to cut down the rotary action of the air which can cause difficulties. This is particularly true if two stacked fans are used, as in some cases the rotary action of the air from the fans can counteract and cut down the total output.

One further point on fan selection is that as the air is required to cool the crop electrical fans should be used, because with most diesel-driven units there is a considerable rise in temperature of the air through the fan (normally around 5°C) which is called the temperature lift. If electricity is not available, a diesel fan will have to be used of the type where the air going through the fan does not pass over the engine. Certain types of centrifugal and belt-driven aerofoil axial fans satisfy these requirements, but are expensive.

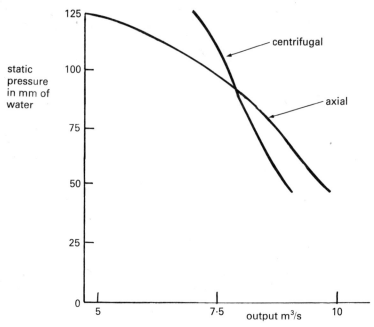

9.1 15 kW axial fan (762 mm) 15 kW centrifugal fan performance curves
(This is a typical example, different models with the same size motor will
give different curves)

In Fig. 9.1 is a graph of a typical centrifugal fan and typical axial
fan with output against pressure. These lines are called the performance curves or fan characteristics. It is advisable to look at
the particular performance curve or fan characteristic of a fan
before deciding to purchase it.

Resistance to Airflow
As has been mentioned previously, when quoting the performance
of a fan it is important to give both the volume produced and the
pressure against which it is working. This pressure or resistance
is measured in a number of different units; a list of the most usual
is given in the appendix, but the simplest and most useful for
potato storage is quoted in millimetres of water. This means that
the pressure exerted by the fan will hold up a column of water of
so many millimetres.

It is measured as shown in Fig. 9.2. There is a U tube of
transparent material with water in it, preferably coloured, as this

makes the readings easier; one end is exposed to atmosphere and
the other end has a tube on it with its end in the main duct. The
difference in the levels of the water is the pressure recorded. The

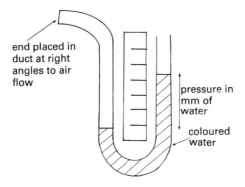

end placed in
duct at right
angles to air
flow

pressure in
mm of
water

coloured
water

9.2 U Tube manometer

tube can be placed anywhere in the main duct, provided it is at
least one fan diameter away from the fan as local turbulence can
give unusual readings.

There are three ways of stating pressure: velocity pressure (Pv)
which is produced by the speed of the air; static pressure (SWG)
which is the resistance of the system against that air flow and total
pressure (TWG) which is the sum of velocity and static pressure.
In potato storage static pressure is what is referred to as pressure
or resistance of the system, and it is for this reason that the tube
in the main duct should be at right angles to the direction of flow.
This ensures that the open tube end does not directly face the
airstream, which might impart to it some 'velocity pressure'.

The resistance of system should be kept low for two reasons:
first, the power absorbed by a fan is proportional to the air delivered, multiplied by pressure, so the higher the pressure the higher
the running costs; secondly, not only will more power be used at
high pressure, but also that power will be converted into heat,
therefore raising the temperature of the air which is being used
for cooling which is clearly not beneficial.

The pressure or resistance of a system is made up of the resistance
of the air flowing down laterals, the main duct, going round bends
and through the lateral cover; this increases with speed which is
why efforts are made to keep the velocity within the ducts down
to 10 m/s or less. A well-designed system has as few bends as
possible and certainly no sharp bends, as these increase resistance.

Clearly, if a dirty crop is put into store, the earth can partially block the apertures in the lateral, increasing the resistance which of course increases the power consumed by the fan and the temperature lift.

The second constituent of the pressure or resistance of the system is the resistance to airflow of the crop itself which should be very low with a clean crop, but as was mentioned earlier is increased by earth and sprouting tubers (by a factor of up to 4). At a typical ventilation rate of 0.02 m^3/s/tonne and a depth of 3 m the resistance of a clean crop would be approximately 0.6 mm SWG per metre depth.

The final constituent is the exhaust vents which should give very little resistance to the system.

In a typical well-designed system the total pressure may well be as low as 12.5 mm SWG with a clean crop, but as dirty crops may occur even in the best-managed stores, it is best to purchase a fan assuming a pressure of 50 mm SWG for bulk stores and 20 mm SWG for box stores.

Ducting

In bulk potato stores using forced ventilation a main duct with smaller ducts (laterals) leading off are used.

There are a number of points to remember when considering the location and dimensions of the main air duct. The optimum length of lateral is 10 m (longer than this requires special design) which means that in a store of any size the main air duct has to go parallel with the longer side of the building. Normally, it will be located in the middle of the building with potatoes on either side and obviously it will require load-bearing walls.

The maximum air speed which should be allowed in the main duct is 10 m/s, therefore the cross-sectional area of the duct must be at least 0.1 m^2 per 1 m^3/s of fan capacity at 50 mm water gauge.

Ideally, the inside surfaces of the main air duct should be smooth as any projections can cause turbulence. If any strengthening members are present, the cross-sectional area should be measured from the inside of them and not the duct walls.

The main air duct should also be large enough for the store operator to be able to walk down easily when it is necessary to open or close laterals. A duct which is difficult to walk down does not encourage careful store management. It is also normal to have lighting in the main duct with an indicator light outside to show whether it is on or off. A stop button for the fan in the main duct is also a useful safety precaution, in case the fan is started with anyone inside, in which case the air pressure will prevent the opening of the duct door for escape purposes.

In some big stores money is saved on the main duct by having one with smaller cross-section with fans at each end, but normally the extra cost of wiring and fan installation will cancel out the money saved on the duct.

Laterals

There are basically two types of laterals (see Fig. 9.3): those which

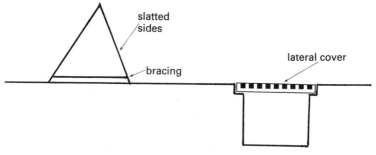

9.3 Above ground and below ground laterals

are above ground which have to be installed and removed when loading and unloading and those which are below ground which allow vehicles to drive over but are more susceptible to blocking with earth. Whatever type is used the cross-sectional area must again be at least $0.1 \, m^2$ per $1 \, m^3/s$ of air. This cross-sectional area requirement applies to the lateral entry as well. Unfortunately certain proprietary lateral systems have entry areas which are only three-quarters or even half the cross-sectional size of the lateral.

As mentioned previously, the optimum length of lateral is 10 m and if the intention is to exceed this the lateral must be stepped or tapered to keep near the same velocity along its length. If this is not done, there will be air starvation at the end of the lateral near the main duct. This means that there will be little if any air through the potato stack near the main duct.

Above ground laterals such as the traditional triangular timber slatted ducts or weldmesh hoops with a hessian covering should be placed at approximately 2 m spacing. These ducts are cheap, but there is always labour in putting down and picking up as well as the possibility of their being damaged. The other main problem is the danger that the lateral might shift when the potatoes are loaded on to it so that no air goes down the laterals.

PLATE 9:5
'A' ducts in a potato store

PLATE 9:6
Potato store with below-ground laterals; in this store the laterals are at 0·9 m centres as the store is also used for grain

Myson

PLATE 9:7
Below-ground lateral covers

Ventec Agricultural Ltd

Below-ground laterals basically consist of a trench cast in the concrete floor with various kinds of lateral cover such as louvred galvanised steel sheets, slatted concrete or wooden bars (100–150 mm wide with gaps of 20 mm between them). Again, the laterals should be at 2 m spacing. Normally, the lateral cover is 0·3 m wide, but allowing for the rebate, this gives an actual width for the lateral itself of 0·25 m. The principal difficulty of this type is the problem of soil blocking either the slots or the lateral underneath. It is advisable to position the lateral covers from the end nearest the main duct, placing a wooden spacer at the far end. This spacer can be removed after the storage season and any trash laying in the bottom of the lateral can be blown to the far end and removed.

A loose brick floor is occasionally used with potatoes. It has the advantage of good air distribution and lower cost than other below-ground systems. The drawback is that the thin cracks between the bricks through which the air passes are easily blocked if there is any dirt so this method is not recommended.

Another type of floor recently introduced is the pallet floor consisting of wooden pallet-sized modules which interlock to form a drying floor. The six bearers support ten slats having 65 mm wide metal inserts between these top planks. This type of floor is quick and easy to lay and can be picked up and put somewhere else if required.

Vents

How the air reaches the fan or leaves the building itself is often an area which is given little consideration, and this is a mistake.

As has been said before, to cut moisture loss from the potatoes to a minimum the relative humidity should be kept high and this cannot be done if air is able to enter or leave the store unintentionally.

Therefore one important consideration is that air should only be able to pass through the vent when required and secondly that light should not be able to penetrate and green the potatoes (if they are uncovered).

The entry of air to the fan house should be through a louvred vent as this will prevent a wind blowing directly against the fan. As a rule of thumb, the size of the entry louvred vent should be 0·135 m² per m³/s of fan capacity.

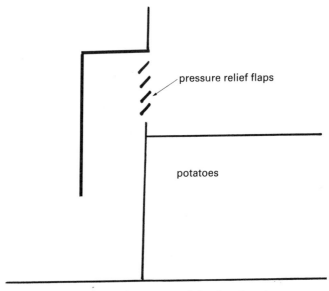

pressure relief flaps

potatoes

9.4 Lightproof pressure relief exhaust vents

The air should be allowed out of the building by using pressure relief flaps which only open when air is being exhausted. This pressure relief system consists of lightweight plastic or aluminium flaps which normally hang vertical but open outwards when the store is being ventilated because when the fans are operating they cause a slight pressure to be built up. The flaps are arranged so that they cannot open inwards and therefore do not let wind or rain into the store. A cowl should also be installed so that there is no light entering the store even when the flaps are open.

PLATE 9:8
Exhaust flap closed

PLATE 9:9
Exhaust flap open

Chandler Farm Electronics and
Installations Ltd

The pressure relief system should allow 0.25 m^2 of free area per m^3/s of fan capacity.[6]

Ventilation Rates

Air is passed through stacks of potatoes for two reasons: one is to cool or heat the stack and the second is to try to ensure that temperature difference is small between top and bottom of the stack.

There are two situations when a stack of potatoes may need to be cooled: firstly, after the curing process; and secondly when the potatoes are warmer than the optimum storage temperature either as a result of respiration heat, warm ambient conditions, or both.

The amount of cooling that each unit volume of air can do is reduced the more unit volumes of air per second are passed through the stack of potatoes. However, the actual cooling efficiency of the air has to be matched with the rate of cooling of the stack at any ventilation rate and the likelihood of air of the right cooling temperature being available. Very high ventilation rates, more than 0.05 m^3/s/tonne can be counter-productive, because the pressure drop in the stack due to ventilation is dependent on the air velocity and so the velocity energy in the air entering the stack is mainly changed into heat within the stack.

Obviously for various requirements different quantities of air are required. For long-term storage of bulk potatoes through to

April, without refrigeration 0·03 m³/s/tonne or more would be suggested, whereas if it is intended to store potatoes only until Christmas, 0·01 m³/s/tonne should be adequate.

Normally a compromise of these ventilation rates is reached and a figure of 0·02 m³/s/tonne is recommended in most cases. Ventilation rates with refrigeration are dealt with under the section on refrigeration.

For box stores, lower ventilation rates can be used as there is no great mass of potatoes all together producing respiration heat. Therefore a ventilation rate can be used of 0·01 m³/s/tonne which is lower than for bulk stored potatoes.

Recirculation
Recirculating the air inside a potato store can help considerably with store management. During periods of non-ventilation a temperature gradient will occur in a potato stack, but this can be considerably lowered by recirculation. Condensation can also be reduced or eliminated by recirculation.

For both condensation reduction and even temperatures the recirculation should be short and frequent, such as five minutes in every hour, as this will stop the problem before it has time to develop, whereas one hour in twelve may not. If recirculation is applied to a stack where a temperature gradient has been allowed to occur, condensation can form on the lower layers of the crop.

The normal method of recirculation is to have a flap between the store air space and the fan house. This flap can be opened and the fan intake with outside air closed, either automatically or manually.

It is possible with appropriate equipment to mix the recirculated air with air from outside. This mixer box arrangement has particular attractions for long-term storage as sometimes during the late storage period, such as the end of March, the only cold air that is available to cool the crop is frosty air, too cold to use by itself, but satisfactory if mixed with recirculated air. How a mixer box works is described in Chapter 1, under seed potato storage.

The recirculation rate need not be as high as for cooling the crop. If the limits on the stack temperature are taken as 0·5°C difference a rate of 0·0075 m³/s/tonne should be sufficient and if a difference of 1·5°C can be tolerated a rate of 0·0025m³/s/tonne is all that is necessary.[7]

Straw Covering for Potatoes
It is conventional practice to provide a covering of straw on top

of the stored potatoes. This straw provides a protection from frost damage, greening, 'drip back' (from the roof of the store) and condensation of moisture in the top layers of the potatoes. The last phenomenon occurs when warm humid air leaves the potato stack and meets cold air above the stack.

A layer of straw of around 0·5 m is normally sufficient. Loose straw or bunches should be used rather than bales which even if of low density are unsatisfactory because condensation can occur on the vertical surfaces all the way down to the potatoes.

Putting the straw down and picking it up is a tedious and at times unpleasant job. It can be made a little easier by putting a light-weight net under the straw—the net should be made of nylon or some other unrottable material. One further disadvantage with using straw is that the store operator has to remove it before the crop can be seen and there is always the danger of inspecting time after time in the same place.

Work is being carried out by the PMB at Sutton Bridge on possible synthetic materials to replace straw, such as nylon quilts. These synthetic materials would have advantages in the speed of putting down and picking up. The capital cost would be higher than for straw and the expected lifespan of these quilts is five years. There can be a tendency for the synthetic filling to bunch up, therefore giving uneven distribution and possible greening of some potatoes near the surface.

If a potato store is well-insulated with the facility for regular recirculation (five minutes every hour) and lightproof vents, no covering should be necessary. Although great care is required at the design stage to achieve these criteria many modern stores are being built which do not need a straw covering.

Examples
The following three examples are given to show the methods of calculating ventilation systems and do not represent a full range of types of potato ventilation.

Example 9.1
Consider a store for 500 tonne of ware potatoes with an intended ventilation rate of 0·02 $m^3/s/tonne$.

Therefore the output of the fan at 50 mm static water gauge = $500 \times 0·02 = 10 \, m^3/s$ (*quantity of potatoes* × *ventilation rate*) *e.g.* a 965 mm 1450 rpm 13 kW fan.

As the maximum permitted velocity in the main duct is 10 m/s, the main duct need only be 1 m² but for the convenience of going inside it a 2 m × 1 m cross-section main duct would be better.

500 tonne of potatoes would have a volume of $500 × 1.5 = 750$ m³ (*quantity of potatoes × bulk density*).

Assuming this main duct is in the centre of a 18 m wide building and the potatoes are stacked 3 m high so the total floor area taken up $= \dfrac{750}{3}$ (*total volume ÷ storage depth*) = 250 m².

The length of main duct must be at least $\dfrac{250}{18-1}$ (*floor area ÷ width less main duct*), = 14.70 (probably 17 m allowing for angle of repose).

The tonnage ventilated by each lateral =

$$\frac{3 \times 2 \times \left(\dfrac{18-1}{2}\right)}{1.5} \left(\begin{array}{c}\textit{storage depth} \times \textit{distance between laterals} \\ \times \textit{ half width of building less main duct} \\ \hline \textit{bulk density}\end{array}\right)$$

$$= 34 \text{ tonne.}$$

Therefore air required for each lateral (*tonnage ventilated × ventilation rate*)

$$= 34 × 0.02$$
$$= 0.68 \text{ m}^3/\text{sec.}$$

If maximum velocity allowed in the lateral is 10 m/s

the cross-section $= \dfrac{0.68}{10}$ (*air required ÷ max velocity*) = 0.068 m².

Assuming a width of 0.25 m for the lateral,

the depth $= \dfrac{0.068}{0.25}$ (*air volume ÷ lateral width*) = 0.27 m;

to be on the safe side give a depth of 0.3 m.

Summarising for a 500 tonne bulk ware store if the building is 18 m wide and the potatoes are stored 3 m deep, with a ventilation rate of 0.02 m³/s/tonne:

Fan   10 m³/s at 50 mm SWG.
Main duct 2 m × 1 m cross section, 17 m long.
Laterals   8.5 m long, 0.3 m × 0.25 m cross section, 14 in number.

Example 9.2

Consider a 1,000 tonne bulk potato store which is for long-term storage. The building is 18 m wide and the potatoes are stored 4·5 m deep.

As the building is for long-term storage a high ventilation rate of 0·03 m^3/s/tonne is used so that any short periods of cold air in the late spring can be utilised.

The whole fan house is a mixer box with mechanical louvred entries from both outside and from the store which can therefore give totally fresh air, totally recirculated air or a mixture (as in Fig. 9.6). Two fans are used as a lower rate is required for recirculation than cooling.

Calculations (similar to Example 9.1)

Total fan output required at 50 mm static water gauge = 1,000 × 0·03 = 30 m^3/s

Therefore two fans of 15 m^3/s at 50 mm water gauge required, *e.g.*, 2 × 965 mm 1,450 rpm 17 kW fan.

As air velocity must be less than 10 m/s in main air duct cross-section must be more than 3 m^2, 3 m × 1·2 m is suggested.

1,000 tonne of potatoes have a volume of 1,000 × 1·5 = 1500 m^3

At a depth of 4·5 m this is a floor area of $\dfrac{1,500}{4·5}$ = 333 m.

As building width is 18 m main duct must be at least $\dfrac{333}{20-1·2}$

= 17·8 m allowing for angle of repose = 22 m approx.

The tonnage ventilated by each lateral = $\dfrac{4·5 \times 2 \times \left(\dfrac{18-1·2}{2}\right)}{1·5}$

= 50·4 tonne.

Therefore air required for each lateral = 50.4 × 0·03 = 1·51 m^3/sec.

If maximum velocity allowed in the lateral is 10 m/s cross-sectional area = $\dfrac{1·51}{10}$ = 0·151 m^2.

Assuming a width of 0·25 m for the lateral

$$\text{the depth} = \frac{0·151}{0·250} = 0·60 \text{ m.}$$

This is really too deep, therefore if a lateral wider by 75 mm is used:

$$\text{the depth} = \frac{0 \cdot 151}{0 \cdot 325} = 0 \cdot 46 \, \text{m}$$

which is satisfactory.

The intake vent for the two fans needs to allow $0 \cdot 135 \, \text{m}^2$ per m^3/s of fan capacity therefore it needs to have at least:

$$0 \cdot 135 \times 30 = 4 \cdot 05 \, \text{m}^2 \text{ cross-sectional area.}$$

The recirculation vent into the fan house should be about the same size; although only one fan will be used for recirculation, this vent will be at right angles to the fan intakes.

The pressure relief flap should allow $0 \cdot 25 \, \text{m}^2$ per m^3/s of fan capacity.

Therefore the total area of pressure relief flap needs to be $0 \cdot 25 \times 30 = 7 \cdot 5 \, \text{m}^2$.

This is of free area and not just the area inside the main frame.

Summarising, for a 1,000 tonne long-term bulk ware store 18 m wide with potatoes 4·5 m deep and a ventilation rate of $0 \cdot 03 \, \text{m}^3/\text{s/tonne}$ the following are the ventilation specifications:

Fan $2 \times 15 \, \text{m}^3/\text{s}$ at 50 mm SWG
Main duct   1·2 m × 3 m cross-section, 22 m long
Laterals   8·4 m long, 0·5 m × 0·325 m cross-section, twenty
              in number.

Example 9.3

Consider a medium-term 500 tonne box store. The building is 18 m long and 12 m wide. As the potatoes are stored in boxes, a lower ventilation rate can be used of $0 \cdot 01 \, \text{m}^3/\text{s/tonne}$.

One method of ventilation would be by way of high-level discharge, low level intake as shown in Fig. 9.7. This will ensure some air distribution in the building. There should be some system of recirculation with an intake just upstream of the fan.

To make the best use of any cold weather a mixer box should be used which can also provide the recirculation.

As the air does not have to be forced through a stack of potatoes the resistance of the system can be taken to be 12·5 mm static water gauge.

$$\text{Total fan output required} = 500 \times 0 \cdot 01 = 5 \, \text{m}^3/\text{s}.$$
Therefore one fan of $5 \, \text{m}^3/\text{s}$ at 12·5 mm SWG required,
e.g., 610 mm   1440 rpm   1·3 kW fan.

TYPES OF POTATO STORE

Types of potato store fall into two basic categories: with and without forced ventilation. The trend over the last twenty years has been to move to forced ventilation systems, but there are still situations where non-forced ventilation may be suitable.

Clamps

This is the simplest method of potato storage and has a low capital cost, but requires a large amount of labour. The potatoes are piled to a ridge approximately 1·75 m high, covered in a layer of straw around 300 mm thick, a sheet of polythene and then earth. There should be a gap left in polythene at the ridge to allow natural ventilation to take place.

Potatoes can be stored in a clamp until around Christmas when sprouting and general deterioration begins to occur. Sprout suppressant can be blown into the clamp in a mist form around about three weeks after clamping.

The main difficulties with clamps are the large amount of labour both at filling and emptying, and the lack of control over the conditions, but for short-term storage where no buildings are available, they can be useful.

Ventilated Clamp or Dickie Pie

A development from the simple clamp is the Dickie Pie (Fig. 9.5)

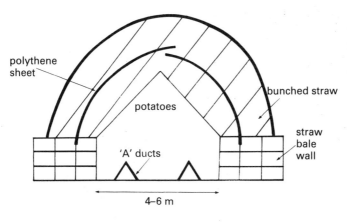

9.5 Dickie pie

which is again built in the field. The potatoes are stored between straw walls covered by thick straw and polythene with ducts providing ventilation.

The Dickie pie should be put on a level well-drained site, preferably close to a hard-core road. The ventilated clamp is normally made by filling in over the straw walls using an elevator; therefore the width is dictated by the reach of the elevator, a typical figure being 6 m. The walls are three bales thick with a sheet of polythene between the single thickness inner wall and the double bale outer wall.

Free convective air movement is allowed by having a duct open at the end to the outside air. For Dickie pies of 4 m width or under one duct is enough, but two are needed for larger clamps. Approximately 0.013 m^2 of cross-sectional area of duct is needed for every 10 tonne stored. In frosty conditions it is important to block off the duct openings to stop frosty air coming into the stack. Top ventilation can be by having the top sheets in an arrangement such as shown in the diagram.

Although this form of potato storage gives more control than a simple clamp, it is still limited. Again there is a large labour content both in the loading and unloading and in the making of the Dickie pie. As a form of temporary storage, it can certainly have its place on some farms.

Indoor Storage without Forced Ventilation

Potatoes are sometimes stored for short periods in a building without forced ventilation. This is normally a temporary measure and can be perfectly satisfactory. As with all types of storage the potatoes should be as dry and clean as possible. The potatoes can be stacked 1·8 m high with ducts at 1·8 m centres, so that convection currents can flow through the crop.

The ends of the ducts should be open to the air although for the first fourteen days or so they should be blocked to allow curing to take place.

The temperature can be monitored by thermometers lowered on strings down polythene tubes with the top of the tube corked.

Bulk Stores

Undoubtedly the most common method of storing potatoes in the UK is the bulk ware store with forced ventilation through laterals off a main duct. Potatoes can be stored to a height of 4·5 m although there are more management problems the deeper they are stored.

The bulk store is of only one basic design with various degrees of sophistication: mixer box, recirculation and refrigeration. Fig. 9.6 shows a bulk store with a mixer box and recirculation.

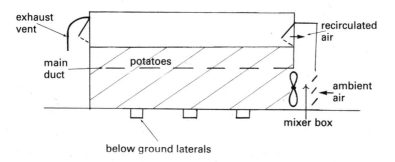

9.6 Bulk potato store with recirculation and mixer box

This type of store can work satsifactorily providing that dry and reasonably soil-free potatoes are put in. There will be a small temperature difference in the stack the size of which will depend on the degree of ventilation and recirculation available.

Thrust walls will be needed.

Table 9.1 summarises some useful facts concerning bulk stores.

Table 9.1

Volume (m^3/t)	1·5
Max storage depth (m)	4·5
Angle of repose	35° (typically)
Load on walls ($kN/m^2/m\ deep$)	1·8[8]
Eaves height	Storage height + 1·0 m

In April 1980 a typical cost of a 1,000 tonne bulk potato store before grant would be £70 to £80/tonne.

Box Stores

The capital cost of box stores is higher than that of a bulk store because of the lower density of potatoes stored per unit volume of store and the cost of the boxes themselves. Box storage can only be justified if the greater degree of flexibility which it gives is fully utilised.

Different varieties, grades or seed stock can be stored in the same building. If potatoes come in with wet soil on them this can be dried off easier in a box than in a bulk store. There are rarely the same temperature differentials in a box as in a bulk store. There are also the advantages in handling that the potatoes can be harvested into the boxes in the field and not touched again until grading. If boxes are used in a co-operative store there is no dispute over whose potatoes are whose, providing the boxes are labelled.

The standard dimensions of boxes are—for a 0·5 tonne box 1,050 mm square base and 900 mm high, and for a 1·0 tonne box 1,200 mm by 1,800 mm base and 900 mm high.

As the boxes take all the thrust there is no need for special thrust walls in a box store.

Table 9.2 summarises some useful facts concerning box stores.

Table 9.2

Volume (m^3/t)	1·7 to 2·2
Max storage depth	4 to 6 boxes
Angle of repose	90°
Load on walls	None
Eaves height	Storage height + 0·5 m

In April 1980 a typical cost for a 1,000 tonne box store including boxes before grant would be £100 to £110/tonne.

The principal difference between different types of box stores is the ventilation system. There are three different types of ventilation system: non-ducted, differential and letter box. All three systems are suitable for mixer box, ambient only or refrigeration. Pressure relief flaps are not shown in the diagram, but are necessary for all three.

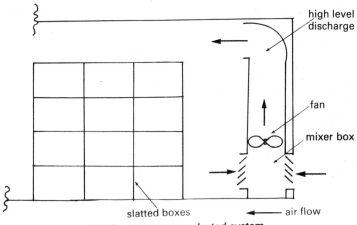

9.7 Box storage non-ducted system

PLATE 9:10
Unloading a potato clamp

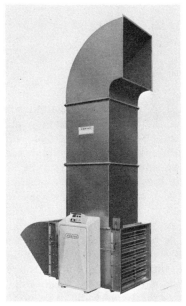

PLATE 9:11
High level discharge system for box stores

Ventec Agricultural Ltd

The non-ducted system (Fig. 9.7) uses the normal slatted-sided potato boxes and the air is brought in to the fan at low level and discharged at high level as shown in the diagram.

The layout of the boxes should be considered carefully to allow ready access to all boxes and adequate ventilation. Gaps of 150 mm should separate each stack. The largest stack that should be put together without a gap is an 8 × 2 ground plan formation as access for inspection is only from the two ends. Air circulation is improved by leaving corner post upstands on the boxes of 50 mm above the top spars.

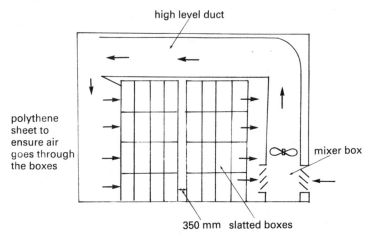

9.8 Box storage differential ventilation system

The differential system (Fig. 9.8) uses the normal slatted box and the air is ducted at high level to the far end from the fan and then pulled back through the boxes. So that the air does not channel through some sets of boxes and not others there should be a gap of 350 mm between each stack of boxes which can be up to 5 or 6 boxes deep. This system does allow for more positive ventilation through the boxes, but does mean a more rigid layout of boxes.

The letter box system (Fig. 9.9) uses boxes with solid sides and only one-way entry pallet bases. The boxes are stacked as shown in the diagram so that the pallet base forms a lateral and the air is positively ventilated through the boxes. The air comes from a duct or plenum chamber into the odd pallet base and is exhausted from even pallet bases. With this system it is possible to go up to

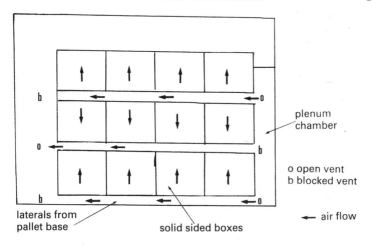

9.9 Box storage letterbox system

ten boxes from the plenum chamber. The advantages of this system are that every box is positively ventilated and very close control of temperature can result. The disadvantages are that normal slatted potato boxes cannot be used, the system relies on careful stacking and there is the cost of a plenum chamber.

References

1. BURTON, W. G., Potatoes—Their Changes and Needs in Storage', *Farm Buildings Digest*, 3 (14), Spring 1968.
2. BURTON, W. G., *Buildings and Equipment for the Storage of Potatoes and Other Vegetable Crops*, I Agr E National Conference, spring 1972.
3. TWISS, P. T. G. and JONES, M. P. (1965), 'A Survey of Wastage in Bulk Stored Maincrop Potatoes in Great Britain', *Eur Potato Journal*, I (3).
4. BURTON, W. G. (1966), *The Potato Veenman en Zonen Wageningen*, 2nd edition, p. 382.
5. MANN, G. (1963), 'The Cooling of Potatoes Stored in Bulk', *Ann. Rep. Ditton and Covent Garden Labs 1962–63*, 30–3.
6. STATHAM, O. J. H. *Sutton Bridge Experimental Report No. 6 part II Control of Environment*, April 1973.
7. BARTLETT, D. I. *Buildings and Equipment for the Storage of Potatoes and Other Vegetable Crops*, I Agr E National Conference, spring 1972.
8. MESSER, J., *Technical Introduction to Farm Building Association Visits*, April 1978.

Chapter 10

POTATO STORAGE (2) HEATING, REFRIGERATION AND HUMIDIFICATION

PSYCHROMETRY

SOME KNOWLEDGE of the subject of psychrometry is important for the design and operation of potato stores. Psychrometry can be said to be the study of the thermodynamic variables in the composition of air and their relationship one with another. During storage, air of different temperatures and humidities can be used and it is useful to predict what the thermodynamic interaction of air in different states will be. It is useful to remember that thermodynamically air has two parts: the dry air and the water vapour.

The prediction of what will occur when air of different temperatures and humidities mix is done with the use of a psychrometric chart. Before considering how to use a psychrometric chart, it is important to know the meaning of the various terms used.

Vapour Pressure
This pressure is the partial pressure exerted by the water-vapour molecules in moist air. Saturated vapour pressure is the pressure exerted by the water-vapour molecules when the air cannot take any more water.

Percentage Saturation
This is the water-vapour pressure of the air in question, divided by the saturated vapour pressure of pure water at the same temperature. It is normally expressed as a percentage and is otherwise known as relative humidity. In potato storage the percentage saturation should be kept as high as possible.

Moisture Content
The moisture content is the weight of water vapour in a dry air/water vapour mixture per unit weight of dry air.

196

Dry-Bulb Temperature

The dry-bulb temperature is the temperature shown by a normal thermometer (mercury in glass, thermocouple) and is the actual temperature of the air. When the word 'temperature' is used, with no explanation or prefix, it is the dry-bulb temperature which is being referred to.

Wet-Bulb Temperature

The wet-bulb temperature is the temperature registered on a thermometer whose sensing element is covered with a wet wick exposed to moving air for at least a minute. On the psychrometric charts the word 'sling' in brackets after 'wet-bulb temperature' indicates that the thermometer was positively aspirated.

Dew-Point Temperature

The dew-point temperature is the temperature at which condensation first occurs when a sample of air is cooled at atmospheric pressure and constant moisture content.

Enthalpy

The enthalpy of a sample of air is the heat content of the dry air and water vapour mixture per unit weight of dry air above a certain reference temperature. In potato storage it is only the difference in enthalpy which is of interest so the reference temperature is of little consequence.

Specific Volume

The specific volume of the dry air/water vapour mixture is the volume per unit weight of dry air. The specific density is the reciprocal of the specific volume figure.

Using a Psychrometric Chart

Although there are a number of different psychrometric charts available, the most commonly used in the UK is the CIBS (Chartered Institution of Building Services) psychrometric chart. (See frontispiece pull-out.)

This chart gives the following six thermodynamic properties: wet-bulb temperature °C (sling), dry-bulb temperature °C, specific enthalpy kJ/kg, moisture content kg/kg (dry air), specific volume and percentage saturation. If any two of these properties are known the state point can be found and the other four read off the chart. The actual use of a psychrometric chart is best shown by an example.

Example 10.1
The dry-bulb temperature = 15°C
The wet-bulb temperature = 12°C.
The vertical line for dry-bulb temperature of 15°C is followed up the chart till the slanting line for 12°C wet bulb is crossed. The percentage saturation can be read off from the curve line which passes through this point as 70 per cent, but putting a ruler horizontally, the moisture content can be read off as 0·0074 kg/kg (dry air). From the steeper sloping lines than for the wet bulb the specific volume can be read off as 0·825 m³/kg and with the help of a ruler the specific enthalpy can be read off as 34 kJ/kg. (Using a large chart from CIBS is considerably easier than using the example chart shown in the frontispiece.)

Example 10.2
What is the resulting temperature and humidity when two equal volume streams of air mix? One is at 10°C and 70% RH (or percentage saturation) the other is at 5°C and 90% RH.
The state point for each air stream is found on the chart and as the specific volumes are similar, it is assumed that there is equal weight of moist air at each point.
The final mixture will have a common specific enthalpy.

Specific enthalpy of air at 10°C 70% RH = 23·5 kJ/kg.
Specific enthalpy of air at 5°C 90% RH = 17·5 kJ/kg
    mean specific enthalpy   = 20·5 kJ/kg.

This fixes one of the parameters for the resulting state point. The final mixture will also have a common moisture content:

moisture content of air at 10°C 70% RH = 0·0054 kg/kg
moisture content of air at 5°C 90% RH = 0·0048 kg/kg.

From these two parameters the resulting air mixture has a temperature of 7·5°C and a percentage saturation 78 per cent.
Other examples which use psychrometric charts are given in the sections on humidification and the theoretical determination of cooling times.

THEORETICAL DETERMINATION OF COOLING TIMES

The use of the following equations will give a guide as to the rate of cooling of a bulk potato crop. This is clearly useful for a store operator. It must be emphasised that it is only a guide as the equations assume a constant air temperature and humidity.

The equations are as follows:

$$DZ = K_2AR + K_1 \tag{1}$$

$$Z = \frac{1000\ APL}{DZ} \tag{2}$$

$$TCH = \frac{Z \times \log_n((T_2 - T_0)\ (T_1 - T_0))}{-0.693} \tag{3}$$

AR = Air ratio   kg/kgh
K_1 = Constant (for potatoes = 57·55)
K_2 = Constant (for potatoes = 148·27)
APL = Air Path Length   m
Z = Half Cooling Time   h
TCH = Cooling Time   h
T_0 = Cooling air temperature
T_1 = Produce starting temperature °C
T_2 = Intended produce temperature °C

An example may be useful.

Example 10.3
Consider 500 tonne of potatoes stored 4 m deep at a temperature of 8°C. The intended temperature is 5°C and the outside air is 4°C. The relative humidity of the air was measured at 90%. Measured speed through the crop, using a vegetable airflow meter is 2 m/min (0·033 m/s). This gives 6·25 m³/s through the crop (0·033 × 1·5 × 500/4) which typically, taking into account losses, would occur with a fan capable of 0·02 m³/s/tonne.

Therefore
Depth in store   = 4 m = APL
Potato Temperature   = 8°C = T_1
Air Temperature   = 4°C = T_0
Required Potato Temperature = 5°C = T_2
Potatoes   = 500 × 1,000 kg.

Air Ratio AR = number of kg of air circulating per hour for each kg of produce.

From a psychrometric chart it can be read off that 1 m^3 of air weighs $1/0 \cdot 79 = 1 \cdot 27 \text{ kg}$.

$$\text{Therefore AR} = \frac{6 \cdot 25 \times 1 \cdot 27 \times 3{,}600}{500 \times 1{,}000} = 0 \cdot 057$$

$$\left(\frac{\text{Ventilation rate} \times \text{density} \times \text{seconds in an hour}}{\text{weight of potatoes in kg}} \right)$$

from equation (1) $DZ = 148 \cdot 27 \times 0 \cdot 057 + 57 \cdot 55$
$$= 66 \cdot 00.$$

Z can now be found from equation (2)

$$Z = \frac{1{,}000 \times 4}{66 \cdot 00} = 60 \cdot 60 \text{ hrs.}$$

TCH can now be found from equation (3) (natural logarithm tables are required or a calculator with the appropriate keys).

$$TCH = \frac{60 \cdot 60 \times \log_n \left(\frac{5 - 4}{8 - 4} \right)}{-0 \cdot 693}$$

$$= \frac{60 \cdot 60 \times -1 \cdot 386}{-0 \cdot 693}$$

$$= 121 \cdot 2 \text{ hours.}$$

WEIGHT LOSS AND HUMIDIFICATION

It is a well-known fact that potatoes lose moisture in storage whenever the relative humidity is below 100 per cent. What is often not realised is just how much weight potatoes sometimes lose in store as there is no obvious difference in the appearance of the tuber until over 5 per cent of the weight is lost.

The amount of water which the air at a certain temperature can pick up is dependent on the difference between the saturated vapour pressure and the actual vapour pressure. This difference in vapour pressures is called the vapour pressure deficit (VPD) and is normally measured in millibars (m bars).

The following table shows the relationship between the vapour pressure deficit and relative humidity at certain temperatures.

PLATE 10:1
Nozzles for humidification

Table 10.1. Vapour pressure deficits and relative humidities at selected
temperatures

Temperature (°C)	0	5	10	15	20	25
Saturated water vapour pressure (m bars)	6·08	8·65	12·16	16·86	23·09	31·28
Water vapour pressure deficit (m bars)	*relative humidity (%)*					
1	83	89	92	94	95	97
2	67	77	83	88	92	94
3	50	65	75	83	87	90
4	34	54	67	77	83	87
5	13	42	59	70	78	84

Except for very low ventilation rates, below $0·003\,m^3/s/tonne$, the weight loss is not related to the air velocity through the potatoes. Clearly, there would be greater weight loss from a continuously ventilated crop than one intermittently blown, as new air is passing over the tubers all the time. This is why over-ventilation should be avoided.

As mentioned under tuber characteristics the weight loss will be in the order of 0·17 per cent per week per millibar VPD. Therefore, if a 500 tonne process potato store was at 10°C 83% RH for fifteen weeks there would be weight loss of 25·5 tonne (5·1%). This weight loss illustrates how important it is to have the correct humidity.

Although high humidity should be held by having a well-sealed store, some farmers, particularly in North America, use humidifiers to help keep up the relative humidity.

Humidifiers

The two basic types of humidifier apply water either in the form of steam or in a mist of fine water droplets.

Steam: If steam is added to an airstream to increase the humidity there will be only a very small change in the air temperature as the water is already in the vapour form. The energy cost required to produce the steam means that humidifying could only be considered for recirculation and not for ventilation with outside air.

Ideally, a steam humidifier has two tanks of water, one tank containing only a very small amount of water which is kept at 90°C by a small thermostatically controlled electric element with a larger element actuated by the humidistat when steam is required and a second larger tank which keeps the first tank at a certain level by a connecting pipe.

This method has quite a high energy requirement and is rarely considered by farmers.

Water droplets: Fine water droplets can be added to the air stream, where they absorb heat, vaporise and increase the air humidity. It is important that only fine water droplets are used otherwise they will not vaporise. Spinning discs, hydraulic nozzles and compressed air/hydraulic nozzles are used.

As well as increasing the humidity of the air, this form of humidification reduces the temperature which can be an advantage but also means that care has to be taken in calculating the amount of water required.

Example 10.5

Air for ventilating a bulk potato store is 5°C 70% RH. How much water is required per m^3/s to increase the humidity to 94%? This calculation is best done using a psychrometric chart.

From 5°C and 70% RH the state point can be found and therefore the specific enthalpy 15 kJ/kg and moisture content 0·0039 kg/kg.

As no heat is being added the specific enthalpy line is followed for 15 kJ/kg until it crosses 94% gives a dry-bulb temperature of

3·5°C and a moisture content of 0·0045 kg/kg. Therefore 0·0006 kg of water are required for every kg of dry air. As the specific volume is approximately 0·8 m³/kg the quantity of water required per m³/s to increase the humidity of the air from 70% to 94% is 0·00075 kg (0·75 g) per second.

Under normal circumstances the maximum quantity of water required per hour for every tonne of potatoes stored will be 0·25 kg.

Great care must be taken to ensure that no water droplets are picked up in the air stream and end on the crop. For this reason it is important to have a well-designed main duct with low air speeds so that any water droplets can drop out. As there is the possibility of water on the floor of the main duct, there must be a drain. After the humidifier switches off, the fan should keep running for fifteen minutes to ensure that there is no surface water on any potatoes.

Control for Humidification
The humidification equipment will be activated by a humidistat if the humidity of the air passing through the main duct drops below a preset figure. The sensor should be well downstream of the humidifier. Unfortunately there are certain problems with most humidistats as they are operated by fibres which expand and contract depending on the humidity. The problem is that in most potato stores there is some dust and when this is picked up by the fibres it changes the amount of expansion and contraction, therefore altering their accuracy. If the humidistat is recalibrated weekly or fortnightly (see section on calibration and positioning instruments), this problem is overcome, but many store operators are reluctant to do this. As mentioned in the section on humidistats there is a new type now on the market with a thin film capacitive sensor, but there is as yet no experience of it in this application.

Owing to the problems with humidification, it is rarely practised in the UK although there are situations where it should be considered seriously. However, it is very important to realise that a reduction in relative humidity means less crop to sell, so care must be taken with the sealing of buildings and in keeping all doors closed whenever possible.

HEATING

Situations Where Heat is Needed
Although most of the emphasis in both seed potato storage and storing the crop for market is on keeping the crop cool, there can

be situations where heat is required. The five cases where heat might be required are: in a very long cold spell, to stop frost damage; avoidance of condensation on the roof; curing the harvested potatoes in adverse conditions and increasing tuber temperature prior to removal from store and when ventilating with very cold air. The first two cases are dealt with in the chapter on insulation, therefore it is only the last three cases which are considered here.

The normal method of curing potatoes is to close up the store and let the temperature rise due to respiration heat from the tubers; however if there is a prolonged harvest, or the weather is particularly cold, a little heat may help.

Heating tubers to a temperature of 7·5°–10°C before removal from store and grading cuts down the possibility of damage and as with curing the standard practice is to close the store up, but again if the store doors are being constantly opened or there are adverse conditions, it is useful to be able to use a little heat.

If no recirculation system is available, the air space above the potatoes should be heated so that it is slightly higher than the tuber temperature. The same applies in a box store. If recirculation is available the appropriate laterals should be open and the heater placed in the air space above the potatoes but not blowing directly on to the potatoes. Care should be taken not to heat the tubers too quickly or the bottom of the stack can overheat.

An unventilated stack will increase in temperature by approximately 0·5°C a day, and with supplementary heating an additional 0·5°C a day should be considered a maximum.

The air leaving the top of a stack of potatoes where supplementary heat has been used at the fan intake may be warmer than the fabric of the building and have a relative humidity of very close to 100 per cent giving a possibility of condensation. This condensation is avoided if the heater is placed in the air space above the potatoes as mentioned previously.

The situation when potatoes require ventilation because they are too warm, but on the other hand the air outside is too cold to be used direct will only occur if a mixer box is not installed. Care has to be taken to ensure that the air is heated just enough to ensure no frost damage occurs, but it must not be heated further or the potatoes will not be cooled. Approximately 1 kW raises the air temperature of 1 m³/s by 0·8°C.

Example 10.6

1,000 tonne store with a ventilation rate of 0·02 m³/s/tonne is at 8°C with a desired temperature of 4°C. The ambient air is −2°C how much heat is required?

$$\text{Size of fan} = 1,000 \times 0.02 = 20 \text{ m}^3/\text{s/tonne}$$
$$\text{Temperature rise required} = 2°C$$
$$\text{Therefore heat needed} = 2 \times 20 \times 1/0\cdot8$$
$$= 50 \text{ kW.}$$

It is worth noting that if the initial air had an RH of 90 per cent raising its temperature to avoid frost damage has reduced the RH to 79 per cent.

This heating of frosty air should only be considered as an emergency.

Types of Heater
There are basically three types of fuel: propane, oil and electricity; the first two would be direct fired while the third would be a heater battery.

Electrical heaters have a low capital cost and are easy to control, particularly if a number of small units make up the whole (for instance 3 × 10 kW), although the fuel is more expensive than in the other two cases. The amount of heat obtained from an oil or propane heater will not be quite as high as would first appear as some fresh air is required for combustion. It can be assumed that oil and propane will give about 75 per cent of their gross calorific value in useful heat.

TABLE 10.2. Gross calorific values for fuels

Fuel	Calorific value	Useful heat
Oil (35 sec)	45,500 kJ/kg	34,125 kJ/kg
Propane	49,000 kJ/kg	36,750 kJ/kg
Electricity	3,600 kJ/kWh	3,600 kJ/kWh

It is very difficult to estimate the heating requirement for curing or prior to grading, but as a guide 3 kW of useful heat per 100 tonne should be adequate.

REFRIGERATION

Refrigeration should only be considered if it is intended to store potatoes beyond the middle of April. It is worth studying the local weather records before making a decision on whether or not to have refrigeration.

Problems can arise if it is intended to use refrigeration just for the remainder of the crop left after mid-April. High air leakage rates and heat gains through the structure can give disproportionately high refrigeration load in relation to the quantity of crop still being stored. These problems can only be overcome if there is careful planning at the initial stages.

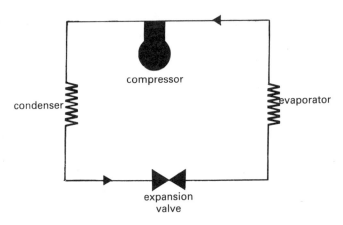

10.1 Vapour compression refrigeration cycle

The basic refrigeration cycle consists of four components: the evaporator, compressor, condenser and expansion valve.

The evaporator is the only part actually in the potato store. The refrigerant goes into the evaporator in a liquid state where it evaporates, absorbing its latent heat of vaporisation from the air around. (The latent heat of vaporisation is the heat required to go from the liquid to the vapour state at the same temperature). The refrigerant then passes in the vapour stage through the compressor and condenser where it becomes a liquid and goes back to the evaporator. There is a pump to move the refrigerant round the circuit.

It is important to ensure the temperature difference across the evaporator coils is not high for two reasons: first, it is vital that the potatoes do not get frost damage and secondly, if the temperature drops too much across the evaporator coils there will be water coming out of the air as condensation, thereby reducing relative humidities in the store. The maximum temperature difference (TD) across the evaporator which should be allowed is 5°C.

PLATE 10:2
Evaporator in box potato store—the store is empty, boxes
are stacked only four high when full

BM Air Services Ltd

Calculation of Refrigeration Load

The refrigeration load for potato stores is made up of five basic
components:
1. The heat gain through the structure (walls, ceiling, floor)
2. The heat gain through air leaking into store
3. The heat produced by the crop
4. The waste heat from electric motors within the cooled area
5. The heat to be removed from any potatoes to bring them down
   to storage temperature.

In most cases the last component can be ignored as normally
the intention of refrigeration in potato stores is to keep the temperature down, the crop having been previously cooled with
ambient air.

Heat gain through structure: this heat gain can be considered in
two parts: the first due to the temperature of the outside air and

the second due to solar heat gain. With the first part the amount of heat gained depends on the thermal transmittance or 'U' value of the walls, roof and floor of the building and the temperature difference between inside the store and the air outside. The second part, which is dealt with in more detail in the chapter on insulation, depends on the colour, orientation of the building, thickness of the walls and roof, the time of year and number of hours of sun in the day.

With long-term storage the heat gain through the structure is the largest component over which there is control.

Heat gain through air leakage: however well-built a store, there will always be some air leakage and the rate of infiltration will be larger in proportion to total volume the smaller the store.

The following table gives some typical figures for infiltration rates.

TABLE 10.3. Infiltration rates

Volume m³ of store	Changes of empty volumes per hour
5·66	1·09
11·32	0·73
28·32	0·43
141·60	0·18
283·20	0·12
566·40	0·09
1,133·00	0·66
2,832·00	0·03

To calculate the heat which has to be removed by refrigeration equipment from the in-leaking air, psychrometric charts should be used.

Obviously if a door is left open in a store the air infiltration rate will leap up. On a store of any size, it is advisable to put in a separate personnel door so that the large main doors do not have to be opened every time the store operator goes in or out. Clearly, it is very important to have close-fitting doors.

Respiration heat: the heat produced by the tubers themselves. This respiration heat is greatly increased if the tubers begin to sprout.

Electrical heat input: All electrical energy used in the store can be assumed to be converted into heat. The main use of electricity in the store will be the circulating fan. With refrigeration the circulating fan need not be as big as for ambient air cooling but of course normally this is not practical. For refrigeration the typical circulation rates are 40 to 60 times the empty volume of the store per hour for a box store and 0.005 m³/s/tonne for a bulk store.

Sometimes another electrical input has to be taken account of and that is the fans on the evaporator in the case of ceiling-mounted units (such as in Fig. 10.2). Most manufacturers take the heat produced by the fans off the quoted cooling capacity but regrettably this is not always done and should be checked when comparing capacities of refrigeration units.

Example 10.7

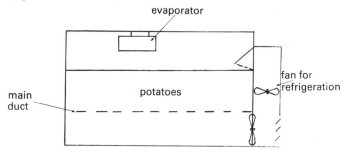

evaporator

main duct

potatoes

fan for refrigeration

10.2 Bulk potato store with refrigeration (note fan for refrigeration in recirculation duct)

Consider a 500 tonne bulk ware potato store with the intention of keeping the potatoes till mid-May and then unloading them in the following two weeks. The store is cooled with ambient air. The store is kept at 5°C, the 'U' value of walls and roof is 0.5 W/m²°C. Store dimensions 14.4 × 19.2 × 5 m to eaves with the roof at 12.5° pitch.

The maximum refrigeration load will occur just before unloading begins. The highest outside temperature expected is 25°C at 60% RH.

Area of walls and roof = 642 m².

The heat gain through the floor is low enough to be neglected.

Heat gain through the walls and roof = total area × U value × temperature difference between inside and out

$$= 642 \times 0.5 \times 20$$
$$= 6,420 \text{ W.}$$

Air infiltration rate depends on total volume which is 1,603 m³ multiplied by the changes in empty volumes per hour.

Infiltration = 1,603 × 0.05 (0.05 is between 0.03 and 0.06 as 1,603 m³ is between 1,133 and 2,832 m³)

$$= 80.15 \text{ m}^3\text{/h}$$
$$= 0.02 \text{ m}^3\text{/s}$$

From a psychrometric chart assuming store condition of 5°C
at 92% RH
the heat gain from air infiltration
= 1,028 W.

A 500 tonne bulk store would probably have one fan capable
of 10 m³/s at 50 mm SWG with a motor of around 10 kW. Therefore
for refrigeration either a separate fan with a lower capacity of
2·5 m³/s (500 × 0·005) at probably only 15 mm SWG should be
used for refrigeration or a two-speed fan is required. If a second
fan is used, this should be put in the recirculation duct.

A fan with an output of 2·5 m³/s at 15 SWG from a manufacturer's
catalogue will produce approximately 500 W. (a 610 mm aerofoil
axial fan at 1420 rpm would be suitable).

The respiration heat at 5°C is approximately 15 W/tonne therefore the total respiration heat is 7500 W.

The total refrigeration loading works out as follows:

Heat leakage through walls	6,420 W
through infiltration	1,028 W
Electrical input	500 W
Respiration heat	7,500 W
TOTAL	15,448 W.

Add 10 per cent safety factor and the size of refrigeration unit
required is one which provides at least 17,000 W (17 kW) of cooling
for a store kept at 5°C.

References
BAKER, F. W., *et al.* 'Psychrometrics Applied to Potato Storage', pp 207–
28, CARGILL, B. F. (ed.), *The Potato Storage* (Michigan State University).

Chapter 11

CONTROL SYSTEMS

THE OBJECT of any control system in a potato store is to keep the temperature and relative humidity of the air blown through the potatoes and therefore the potatoes themselves as near the intended conditions as possible. Provided that the structure and ventilation are adequate the amount of storage losses will depend on how well the store is managed. A control system should help the store operator in this task.

A control system will help the operator make the most of the available conditions and relieve him of much of the routine work. This does not mean that the operator should not regularly inspect the crop and take tuber temperatures, and make appropriate adjustments in the light of current conditions.

A control system, whether totally automatic, semi-automatic or manual should be considered as a management aid and not an end in itself. Often a control system is criticised for not functioning properly when the difficulty is that it was either not installed correctly and instruments were badly positioned, or there was a misunderstanding over what the system could do, the operator did not understand how to operate the system or the system had not been correctly maintained. Therefore it is important to ensure that the operator is clear on what exactly the control system does, how to operate it and how it functions.

Regardless of the level of sophistication of the control system it is still advisable to have a number of mercury-in-glass thermometers in the store.

These mercury-in-glass thermometers should be put in tubes as indicated in Fig. 11.1. They should be put at a depth of about 0·5 m below the surface as this is the depth of highest temperature. Plasticine should be put round the bulb of the thermometer to give a larger thermal mass so that it behaves more like a tuber. If these thermometers are the only way of indicating the stack temperature there should be one for every 50 tonne and if a remote temperature indicator is installed there should be one for every 100 tonne.

Before going any further a glossary of some of the terms used in control and instrumentation is given.

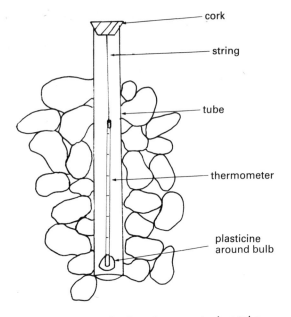

11.1 Mercury-in-glass thermometer in a tube

GLOSSARY

Ambient Air
  Outside Air

Recirculation
  'Closed circuit' ventilation with air that has already passed through the crop.

Hunting
  A control system 'hunts' if the setting is such that the difference in temperature between the fan/heater coming on and going off is so small that the system is constantly switching on and off. This causes undue wear and can be avoided by correct setting of the controls.

Differential
  A differential is the band between the on and off positions of a controlled piece of equipment. For example a heater could be set to switch on at 0°C and switch off at 2°C. The difference

between these figures is the differential. If there was no difference the heater would be constantly switching on and off (*i.e.* hunting).

On/Off Thermostat

This type of thermostat is basically a temperature-controlled switch such that at a certain temperature, which can be manually set, it switches the power either on or off. This type of thermostat has a temperature band (sometimes called a differential) so that it does not switch on and off at exactly the same point when the temperature is going up as coming down. This is done to avoid very rapid switching on and off. The band is normally at least 1°C and can be manually adjusted on most models.

This thermostat can be used for a variety of purposes which might include shutting off fans at low temperatures ('frost stat'), switching on heaters or switching on fans as temperatures rise.

Differential Thermostat

This unit compares the temperature of the crop with the outside air. Whenever the former exceeds the latter by a preset number of degrees, typically 2–3°C, contact is made so that a ventilating fan may be started.

Similarly the contact is broken when the stack and ambient air approach the same temperature or when the ambient temperature is greater than that of the stack.

Hygrometer

An instrument for measuring relative humidity. It is important to check and recalibrate this instrument at least once a month as the sensing element—usually hair—can easily become dirty or damaged.

Thermograph

An instrument which records temperature on a chart for a given period.

Thermo-Hydrograph

Same as above but also records the relative humidity, with a second pen arm controlled by the tension of a hair sensing element.

Humidistat

Basically the same as a thermostat in function but it is actuated by changes in relative humidity.

Manual Control System

This system is one where all operations such as switching fans or heaters on or off is done by the store operator.

Semi-Automatic Control System

A system incorporating a limited degree of automation with manual control. It is normally considered to be one where there is one control component such as a thermostat which brings a fan on if the potatoes are too warm regardless of whether the air temperature is suitable.

Automatic Control System

A system capable of maintaining preset store conditions without operator assistance. Manual override arrangements are always provided.

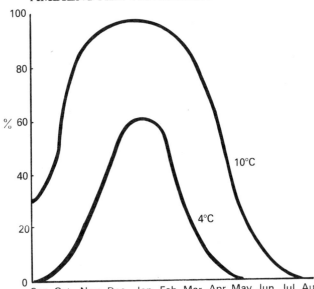

AMBIENT AIR VENTILATION CONTROL

11.2 Percentage of time that store temperature is above ambient temperature (taken for Cambridge, UK)

For much of the winter period the ambient air temperature is lower than the required temperature for crop storage; this difference can be used to keep the crop cool. Any control system should be able to ensure that full advantage can be taken of the cooling potential of the outside air, always provided that safeguards against frost damage are included.

A simple automatic control system consists of three thermostats; frost, store and differential as shown controlling a fan in the block diagrams below.

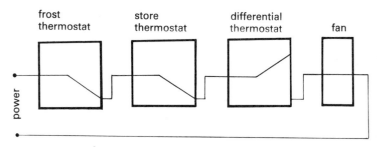

11.3 Fan off, differential thermostat not satisfied

In Fig. 11.3 the store thermostat is calling for cold air and the frost thermostat is on ('satisfied') that the air is above 0°C but the differential thermostat is not satisfied that there is a large enough difference, so the fan does not come on.

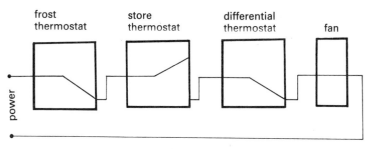

11.4 Fan off, store thermostat not satisfied

In Fig. 11.4 again the fan is off but this time the differential thermostat and the frost thermostat are 'satisfied' but the store thermostat is in the off position because the store is at the correct temperature. Therefore the fan does not come on.

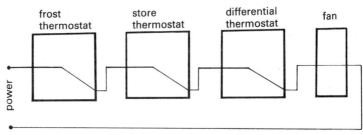

11.5 Fan on, system satisfied

In Fig. 11.5 all three thermostats are satisfied so the fan comes on and will stay on until one of the thermostats switches it off. This control system could be used for ware, process and sprouting potatoes.

Ware Potatoes

Newly harvested potatoes normally require 'curing'. Therefore initially the temperature of potatoes is allowed to rise to around 15°C for about 10–14 days for the wounds to heal.

For this situation the ventilation equipment is normally switched off or the store thermostat is set at a temperature, such as 20°C, which is well above the normal curing temperature. During the curing period the temperature should be still monitored.

After the curing period the store thermostat should be manually set at 4–5°C, the differential thermostat should be put to a minimum differential (probably 2–3°C) and the frost thermostat to −1°C.

If the temperature in the store goes above 4–5°C the store thermostat will call for cooling. If the temperature outside is 2°C lower than in the store, the differential thermostat will allow the fan to come on.

This situation will continue until either the store is below 4–5°C or the difference between the store and the outside is less then 2°C when the fan will switch off.

However, if the temperature outside goes below −1°C the frost thermostat switches off the fan and regardless of what the other two thermostats say the fan will not go on again until the temperature rises above −1°C. It is in this situation that a mixer box can be most useful (see Chapter 1 and Fig. 1.2 for information on mixer boxes).

Processed Potatoes (for crisping and chipping)

As with ware potatoes, the first operation is to heal the wounds on the potato so a curing period of 10–14 days is needed at around

PLATE 11:1
Control panel for ambient ventilation control

Ventec Agricultural Ltd

15°C. The store thermostat should be manually set at 20°C with the differential thermostat giving a 3°C differential and the frost thermostat set at 1°C.

During the storage period it is important that the temperature does not drop below about 7°C to maintain a lower sugar content, although much above this figure will produce high losses through evaporation. Therefore the store thermostat should be set at 7–8°C.

The frost thermostat should be set at 1°C to 5°C depending on time of year and the cool air available. Though obviously it is important not to have the potatoes below about 4°C for any period of time, it is important to avoid high evaporative loss which will occur if long periods of blowing are used with small temperature differentials. Therefore a compromise has to be reached on the minimum ventilation temperature. This is a management decision and will probably need adjustment of the frost thermostat at various times during the season.

Where automatic control systems are to be installed, the ventilation rate must be high enough to avoid prolonged blowing and to keep moisture loss to a minimum.

How the actual control system works will be the same as with ware potatoes. Take the case where the differential thermostat differential is set at 3°C and the store thermostat will call for cooling. If the temperature outside is 3°C lower than the store, the differential thermostat will allow the fan to come on. This situation will continue until either the store is below 8°C or the difference between the store and the outside is less than 3°C when the fan will switch off. As before the frost thermostat will switch the whole system off if the temperature outside drops below 3°C.

Recirculation and mixing greatly help in the storage of crisp and chipping potatoes and heat is also sometimes needed.

Seed Potatoes

As with the ware and processed potatoes, the first operation is to heal the wounds on the potatoes so a curing period of 10–14 days is needed at around 15°C. Again the store thermostat should be manually set at 20°C with the other thermostats at 2°C differential and the frost thermostat at 1°C.

For sprouting potatoes there are two periods after the initial curing and opening of tuber eyes, the first a period when sprouting of potatoes is to be slowed down considerably or halted and the second period when the sprouts are to be encouraged.

During the first period the temperature should be kept below 3–4°C as above this temperature sprouting will begin. Therefore the store thermostat should be set at 4°C, the differential to 2°C and the frost to −1°C.

For the sprouting period the store thermostat should be set to 8°C to encourage the potatoes to sprout slowly. The differential thermostat should be left as before. Store temperature can be regulated to suit variety and conditions.

The acutal functioning of the control system is the same as in the previous examples. Recirculation at regular intervals to avoid temperature variations within the store is advisable.

Further Control

So far only the very basic control system has been described and in many situations some greater amount of control is beneficial.

Recirculation is one example of this greater control where the air for the fan comes from the store itself. Recirculation is useful:
1. When crop is warmer than the intended storage temperature and the outside air is too cold for safe use.
2. To ensure an even temperature throughout the store. A time-clock would probably be used on the recirculation system so that the fan was on for, say, ten minutes in every sixty.

Even better flexibility can be achieved using a mixer box so that even very cold outside air can be used, mixed with some of the warmer store air. The actual proportions can be controlled automatically by the variable position of the damper or slide (see Fig. 1.2).

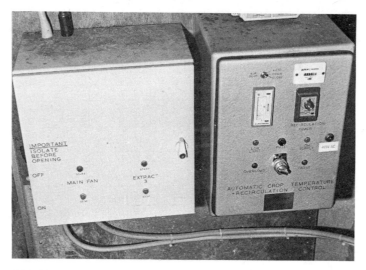

PLATE 11:2
Control panel for ambient ventilation and recirculation

Chandler Farm Electronics and Installations Ltd

Example—Potato Sprouting Store

In this example of a control system for a potato sprouting store a recirculation system and a heater have been included. The ventilation system can be changed automatically from ambient air to recirculation.

As before, the frost thermostat should be set at −1°C, the differential at 2°C and the store thermostat during the store period at 4°C.

If the temperature in the store goes above 4°C the store thermostat will call for cooling. If the temperature outside is 2°C lower than the store, the differential thermostat will allow the fan to come on. This situation will continue until either the store is below 4°C or the difference between the store and the outside air is less than 2°C when the fan will stop ventilating and change to recirculation.

The situation in Fig. 11.6 is when the recirculation is taking place as the difference between the inside and the outside air is less than 2°C.

However, if the temperature outside goes below −1°C the frost thermostat switches off and regardless of what the store and dif-

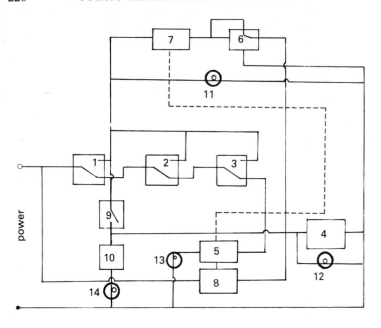

11.6 Ambient air ventilation control with heater and recirculation

KEY
1. *Outside frost thermostat*
2. *Store thermostat*
3. *Differential thermostat*
4. *Fan*
5. *Damper motor, normally closed*
6. *Time switch, recirculation only Auto/Manual*
7. *Damper motor auxiliary switch, contacts made when damper closed* ⎫ *same switch*
8. *Damper motor auxillary switch, contacts made when damper open* ⎭
9. *Inside frost thermostat*
10. *Heater*
11. *Recirculation indicator (Red light)*
12. *Fan indicator (Green light)*
13. *Ventilate indicator (White light)*
14. *Heater indicator (Blue light)*

Dotted line indicates that 5, 7 and 8 are physically together

ferential thermostat say, the fan will continue on recirculation. If the weather continues very cold, the temperature inside the store drops below 0°C, the inside froststat makes contact and the heater comes on. The heater stays on until the store temperature rises above 1°C again.

MEASURING EQUIPMENT

To be able to manage any potato store it is important to be able to measure what is going on, and the four principal parameters are temperature, humidity, air flow and pressure. The measurement of air pressure has already been considered in Chapter 9.

Temperature: the knowledge of temperature is fundamental for store management. It can be measured in one of three ways which are of concern in potato storage: mercury-in-glass thermometers, thermocouples or thermistors.

A good quality mercury-in-glass thermometer is accurate to less than one degree centigrade although it cannot be read remotely and is too fragile to be pushed into tubers. They are reliable and any store should have some installed in the manner which has been shown at the beginning of this chapter (Fig. 11.1).

Thermocouples are formed by the junction of two metals, normally copper–constantan which produces an electromotive force by the difference in the temperature between two junctions; one a reference junction, normally inside the measuring equipment and the second at the point of temperature measurement. The electromotive force in millivolts is expressed on the measuring instrument as temperature. A thermocouple can follow a quickly changing temperature, can be remotely read and can be put inside a needle probe to measure the temperature in the centre of tubers. The main problem with thermocouples is that their accuracy can drift and should be checked before each season. Details on how this should be done are given on page 224, under 'Calibrating and Positioning Instruments'.

Thermistor temperature measurement depends on the fact that the electrical resistance of the thermistor changes with temperature. Therefore the current passing through from a given electrical (normally battery) source also varies with temperature and can be expressed on the measuring equipment directly as temperature. Its advantages and disadvantages are similar to those of a thermocouple.

Humidity: as has been mentioned many times it is important to maintain a high humidity to cut down moisture loss of the stored crop to a minimum. Therefore it is vital to be able to measure it. It can be measured in one of three ways which are of concern in potato-storage: expansion hygrometers, wet and dry bulb hygrometers and a thin film capacitative sensor. Expansion/contraction hygrometers contain moisture-sensitive fibres, commonly hair or cotton, which produce minute movement in response to changes in atmospheric humidity. The movements of the fibres are amplified to register relative humidity on a dial or chart display. The calibration of these instruments is easily upset by dust or soil particles which get lodged between the fibres. Unfortunately these conditions often exist in vegetable stores which makes it useless to employ these instruments unless frequent attention (at least once a fortnight) is paid to cleanliness.

Wet and dry bulb hygrometers have two thermometers, thermocouples or thermistors, one of which has a wick and a small water reservoir. The evaporation of water on the wick lowers the temperature in relation to the dry bulb and, using a relative humidity slide rule or a psychrometric chart, the two temperatures recorded can be converted into a relative humidity figure. To attain accurate results the air should be passing over the two thermometers and the most common hygrometer used is the whirling type which looks like a football rattle. This equipment should be whirled until a steady reading is obtained. The wet bulb will take time to cool, normally less than two minutes. The wick should be replaced if it becomes dirty or salty from deposits left by the water. Ideally, distilled water should be used.

The thin film capacitative sensor relies on the capacitance varying with relative humidity. This form of humidity measurement which can also be directly incorporated in a humidistat is a recent introduction on the market, and it has a claimed accuracy of ± 1 per cent.

Air flow: the actual airflow through a fan in situ is difficult to measure accurately. Provided that the fan output quoted by the manufacturers is to an appropriate national standard such as a British Standard for British equipment or an American Standard for American equipment the fan can be assumed to be giving the correct airflow providing it is correctly installed. Therefore measuring air flows through fans should be left to the specialist.

The airflow through the crop is a different matter and clearly it can be very useful for a store operator to know how much air is passing through the crop. The instrument used is called a vegetable airflow meter and actually measures air velocity through the crop, which can by consideration of the depth and density of the potatoes be converted into airflow per tonne of crop.

As the resistance to airflow of potatoes is low any instrument put on the surface will have a comparably high resistance and therefore the air will go round it rather than through it. Further, it is difficult to arrange a good seal between the potatoes and the body of the instrument. For this reason the vegetable airflow meter

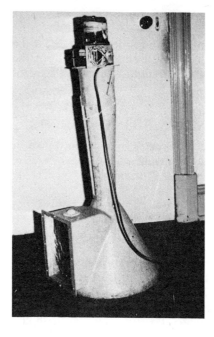

PLATE 11:3
Vegetable airflow meter showing levelling bubble, fan and flap

has a fan on it sucking air upwards which compensates for the resistance. To operate the meter it must be put down level on the crop (there is a levelling bubble), the fan is switched on and then a shutter worked so that with the help of an indicating flap the fan is just compensating for the resistance of the instrument—no more, no less. The air velocity is then read off by the height of a metal disc on a taut wire in the meter.

For a stack of potatoes 4·5m deep being ventilated at 0·02 m³/s/tonne the air velocity will be 0·06 m/s.

CHOICE OF THERMOSTATS AND HUMIDISTATS

Any thermostat which is used in potato storage must be robust and for this reason a domestic thermostat is not suitable. It must be easy to see at what temperature the thermostat is set and also it should not be difficult to alter the setting. It should be also possible to alter the differential.

The electronic thermostat has two main advantages over the electromechanical type; firstly there can be more than one sensor per thermostat, a factor of increasing importance with store size and secondly the use of cable rather than a capillary makes the siting and removal at unloading more flexible.

The subject of control of humidification is dealt with under the section on humidification but it is worth emphasising again the problem of keeping humidistats accurate without frequent calibration.

CALIBRATING AND POSITIONING INSTRUMENTS

Instruments for controlling and monitoring a store can make or lose a lot of money for the farmer depending on whether they are functioning properly or not. Therefore it is important to check *all* instruments before each storage season.

Checking instruments need not take very long, but if this is not done the farm is taking an unnecessary gamble.

Positioning of Instruments

Not only is accuracy of instruments important, but also their position. For example a low limit thermostat is of no use if it is placed in a position where the air is warmer than that going through the fan or where the sun can fall directly on it.

The sensing element or elements of a store thermostat should be placed at two-thirds of the stack height. The element should have some form of thermal lagging to prevent 'hunting' of the system. There are a number of systems now on the market with more than one sensing element for the store thermostat. Some of these are controlled by the mean of the sensed temperatures and some are controlled by the most extreme temperature sensed by any of the elements. At present there is not enough information available to say whether there is a definite advantage for any one of these two multi-sensing units. However, it is obvious that the more sensing elements one has in the crop, the more accurate measurement of temperature one will have.

If a humidistat is fitted it should be placed just downstream of the fan in the main duct so that it is receiving a representative sample of the fan air.

Checking Procedure for Temperature Measuring Instruments

A good quality mercury-in-glass thermometer which complies with a British Standard should be obtained specifically for checking all temperature measuring equipment.

The temperature sensors and thermometer should all be placed just below (say 50 mm) the surface of a bucket of water and given about fifteen minutes to come into equilibrium. It is more practical to check at a temperature near that at which the equipment will be used. A stirrer is used to ensure that the temperature of the water is even throughout the bucket.

Temperatures registered by the equipment are compared against the mercury-in-glass thermometer.

The continued use of equipment known to register the wrong temperature (say by more than 1°C out of true) is not advisable, particularly if there is more than one operator.

Checking Procedure for Thermostats
In the case of thermostats which do not give a direct read-out of temperature the actual operating temperature can be difficult to obtain. It is done by starting with the changeover temperature at the minimum setting and turning the adjusting knob or screw up until a 'click' is heard. This temperature is noted and the adjuster is turned down until another 'click' is heard and this temperature is also noted. The mean of these two readings is the temperature at which the thermostat is registering.

The difference between the two temperatures noted is called the differential and should be set at 1–1·5°C. If the differential is too small the system will keep switching on and off (hunting). If the differential is too large there will be big temperature variations in the store.

Checking Procedure for Humidity Measuring Instruments
1.   Wet and dry bulb hygrometers (psychrometers). These are normally made from two mercury-in-glass thermometers and a wick with a small water reservoir.

It is important to check that the sensors register temperature accurately although in the case of mercury-in-glass thermometers they are unlikely to change.

The water retention properties of wicks are reduced by dust and salts deposits so it is advisable to wash or renew wicks when they are dirty and to use distilled water in the reservoir.
2. Expansion/contraction hygrometers (normally with a dial read-out). Every fortnight the instrument should be washed, left to dry and recalibrated by setting to 100% immediately after having the element wrapped in a wet cloth for at least thirty minutes.

EXAMPLES OF CONTROL SYSTEMS

Having considered some of the principles of control systems examples are now given of three proprietory systems available with differing facilities and degrees of sophistication. These are just

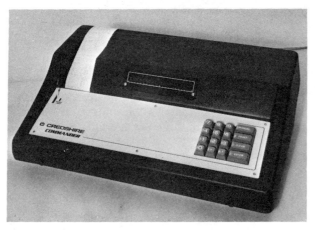

PLATE 11:4
Credshire Commander with print-out facility

various examples of systems used in UK and omission of any type or supplier is no criticism of their product.

Clearly the justifiable cost for a control system and requirements will vary between stores so all three examples would be the correct type of equipment for different stores.

The first example of a control system is the Selectair by Cornercroft (Agricultural) Ltd.

This is a standard ambient ventilation control system which has a low limit thermostat and differential thermostat and up to sixteen probes in the stack itself. The system will call for cooling if any of the probes is too high.

There is also a digital display so that the temperature of any probe and ambient temperature can be seen if required.

The second example of a control system is the Cropminder by Ventec (Agricultural) Ltd.

This system can have up to sixty-four probes and is based on scanning the probes rather than an averaging system. Each of the sixty-four sensors can be given a set temperature so different parts of the stack can be kept at different temperatures if required: this can be useful if part of the store is being cured and another part is being kept at storage temperature.

The Cropminder works on the ambient air ventilation control system, comparing store with ambient temperatures. Also it can bring on intermittent recirculation if required and control mixing of air to make the most of ambient conditions.

The operator can obtain a digital display of sensor temperatures, sensor set temperatures, sensor number, time and time that the fan has operated, fan operating.

Additions to this control system are an alarm for power failure and a print-out facility for sensor temperatures and set temperatures either on demand or every twenty-four hours.

The final example of a control system is the Commander by Credshire Ltd.

This system can have up to a thousand probes and has a system which scans and considers all the probes being used individually. As with the previous example each of the sensors can be set to a different temperature if required. It is not necessary to use all the sensors, but just those required.

All the probes in this control system are on the same cable loop which saves a considerable amount of money on wiring and installation.

Up to sixteen different fans can be controlled so that only the fan or fans relevant to any high temperature would be brought on. The system works as a normal ambient ventilation control system.

The operator can obtain a digital display of a particular sensor, date, set temperature or scan limit.

There is a print-out facility which can give records at any time interval up to twenty-four hours or on demand. It will give the time and date of the print-out as well. Alongside each temperature is an analogue representation of how close it is to the desired temperature: the more dashes, up to five, the further away. After very poor temperatures a blank line is left and a star printed. These reminders are useful for the operator of a large store in helping to point out possible trouble spots.

SUMMARY

A control system is only an aid to management and does not replace the store operator.

Controls enable better use to be made of available conditions than pure manual control.

It is important that the store operator knows how the control system functions and how to alter the settings of the components such as thermostats, when required.

The accuracy of all temperature and humidity measuring equipment must be checked and recalibrated every year, or, in the case of expansion/contraction humidity equipment, fortnightly.

Chapter 12

THE SELECTION AND ECONOMICS OF INSULATION AND THE AVOIDANCE OF CONDENSATION

REASONS FOR INSULATION

THERE ARE three main reasons why the walls and ceiling of potato stores should be insulated: firstly to keep the heat or cold (depending on requirements) within the potato store itself; secondly to minimise temperature fluctuations due to outside weather conditions, and thirdly to eliminate condensation occurring on the interior surfaces of the store.

Therefore correct insulation helps the store operator to maintain the right environmental conditions for the storage of potatoes.

SYMBOLS USED IN INSULATION

There are a number of different ways of expressing the insulation value of materials and structures and obviously it is important that it is known which term is being used.

Thermal Transmittance (U)

The thermal transmittance represents the total heat flow through a material or combination of materials. The units for U are $W/m^2{}^\circ C$. This is the most important insulation symbol and takes into account all the separate factors which influence the insulation value of a wall or ceiling including air movement in the cavity.

Example 12.1

With the 'U' value the heat flow through a wall can be calculated. For instance if a wall with an area (A) of $50\,m^2$ has a 'U' value of $0.75\,W/m^2{}^\circ C$ and the inside temperature (T_i) is 5°C and the outside temperature (T_0) is 15°C (see Fig. 12.1) the heat flow (Q) will be:

228

Area of wall × 'U' value × temperature difference

$Q = AU (T_0 - T_i)$

$= 50 \times 0.75 \times 10$

$= 375$ W.

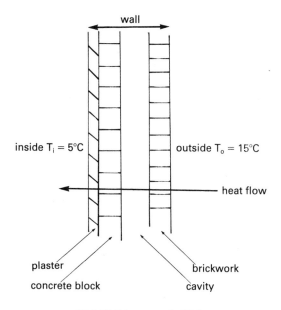

12.1 Wall in example 12.1

This means there will be a heat flow through the wall of 375 W from outside to inside.

Thermal Conductivity (k)
The thermal conductivity of a material is a specific property of that material and is defined as the quantity of heat in Watts flowing through 1 square metre of the material 1 m thick when there is a temperature difference of 1°C between the faces. The units of k are W/m°C. The lower the k value of a material the higher is its insulation efficiency.

Thermal Resistivity (1/k)
This is the reciprocal of thermal conductivity and multiplied by the thickness of the material considered gives the thermal resistance.

Thermal Resistance (R)

The thermal resistance represents the measure of the resistance to heat flow through a material or combination of materials. The units for R are $m^2 °C/W$.

$$\text{Thermal resistance} = \frac{\text{thickness of material}}{\text{thermal conductivity of material}} = \frac{L}{k}$$

In any insulation calculations it is the inside and outside temperatures which are used as the actual surface temperature is not normally known. When heat goes from inside to outside it first goes into the structure, then through the structure and then out from the structure. These inside and outside surfaces actually provide a resistance to heat flow and the 'U' value of a wall or whatever takes them into account.

This surface resistance can be important particularly in a poorly insulated structure. The 'U' value is the only expression of insulation which takes surface resistance into account.

$$U = \frac{1}{\text{total sum of the thermal resistances}}$$

Therefore for calculation the heat loss or heat gain of a building it is the 'U' values of the walls, roof and ceiling which are required.

The heat transmission through a structure is dependent on three factors: the thermal transmittance (the 'U' value), the surface area of the structure (A) and the temperature difference between inside and outside ($T_0 - T_i$).

This can be expressed as an equation:

$$Q = UA (T_0 - T_i).$$

Floors: there are many factors influencing the heat flow through a solid floor. The main ones are the level of the water table, the type of subsoil, the size and shape of the floor and the period that the building has been maintained at the required temperature. As much of the heat flow can be considered to have passed through the edge of the floor the effective 'surface area' can be taken as a one metre strip around the edge of the building.

Insulation of the edge of the floor 0·6 m to 1·0 m deep will typically reduce heat flow by between 10 per cent and 20 per cent of the loss through the floor compared with an uninsulated floor.

How to Calculate the Heat Transmission through a Structure

This is best illustrated by an example.

Figures for the thermal conductivity of standard materials are given in Appendix I.

Example 12.2
Consider the case of a ware potato store:
dimensions 27 m × 18 m; 4 m to eaves and 5·8 m to the pitch. The walls are made of corrugated asbestos sheeting, 50 mm of extruded polystyrene with its own vapour seal and galvanised steel thrust walls to 3 m.

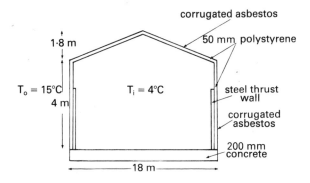

12.2 Building in example 12.2

The ceiling is corrugated asbestos sheeting and 50 mm of extruded polystyrene. The floor is 200 mm of concrete (see Fig. 12.2). Assume a store temperature of 4°C and an ambient temperature of 15°C.
Calculating the 'U' values for the walls, ceiling and floor goes as follows.

1. Walls

	Thickness L(m)	Thermal conductivity k(W/m°C)	Thermal resistance $R(L/k)(m^2°C/W)$
Asbestos sheeting	0·010	0·230	0·043
Extruded polystyrene	0·050	0·029	1·720
Galvanised steel	0·005	50	0·0001
Surface resistance (vertical)			0·176
	Total Resistance		1·939

The galvanised steel thrust walls have such a low thermal resistance that in practice it can be ignored in insulation calculations.

$$\text{'U' value} = \frac{1}{\text{Total Resistance}} = \frac{1}{1 \cdot 939} = 0 \cdot 52 \text{ W/m}^2{}^\circ\text{C}$$

2. Roof

	Thickness L(m)	Thermal conductivity k(W/m°C)	Thermal resistance R(L/k)(m²°C/W)
Asbestos sheeting	0·010	0·230	0·043
Extruded polystyrene	0·050	0·029	1·720
Surface resistance for roof)			0·150
	Total Resistance		1·913

$$\text{'U' value} = \frac{1}{\text{Total Resistance}} = \frac{1}{1 \cdot 913} = 0 \cdot 52 \text{ W/m}^2{}^\circ\text{C}$$

As the rate of heat flow is low through soil normally only the metre round the edge is considered as 'surface area'.

3. Floor

	Thickness L(m)	Thermal conductivity k (W/m°C)	Thermal resistance R(L/k)(m²°C/W)
Concrete	0·2	0·8	0·250
Surface resistance			0·150
	Total Resistance		0·400

$$\text{'U' value} = \frac{1}{\text{Total Resistance}} = \frac{1}{0 \cdot 4} = 2 \cdot 5 \text{ W/m}^2{}^\circ\text{C}$$

Therefore total area is:

Area of walls	= 392 m²
Area of roof	= 496 m²
Area of concrete strip around edge of floor	= 86 m²

Therefore heat loss is:

$$\left[\begin{array}{c} 392 \times 0{\cdot}52 \times (15 - 4) \\ \text{walls} \end{array}\right] + \left[\begin{array}{c} 496 \times 0{\cdot}52 \times (15 - 4) \\ \text{roof} \end{array}\right]$$

$$+ \left[\begin{array}{c} 86 \times 2{\cdot}5 \times (15 - 4) \\ \text{floor} \end{array}\right]$$

$$= 2242 + 2837 + 2365$$

$$= 7444 \text{ W}$$

Heat transmission through structure = 7,444 W.

Air Tightness

It is important not to let air of a different temperature or relative humidity into the store or this nullifies the effect of the insulation. Therefore care must be taken to ensure that all cracks are sealed and that doors are a good fit and never left open when it is not necessary. A separate personnel door should be fitted so that the main doors do not have to be opened when the crop is inspected.

Example 12.3

If the same building is considered as in Example 12.2 it has a total empty volume of 2,381 m^3. If the building is well sealed the air infiltration rate can be estimated from Table 10.3 as 0·05 air changes an hour. Assuming air of 4°C and 95% RH inside the building and 15°C 75% RH outside (the same temperatures as Example 12.2) this air infiltration gives a heat-in leakage of 724 W. This is about 10 per cent of the heat transmission through the structure.

A poorly sealed building could easily have an air infiltration rate of five times that of a well-sealed building. This gives a heat-in leakage of about 50 per cent of the heat transmission through the structure and begins to cut down significantly the advantage gained by having a well-insulated building.

Conservation of Heat or Cold

At all times of year, whether sprouting, ware or crisping potatoes are being considered, there can be a problem of retaining the correct temperature. Table 12.1 gives the number of degree days above and below the intended storage temperature for Cambridge, UK. (See Appendix II for other locations).

Degree days are a measure of both time and temperature. For instance if the mean temperature for a day is 10°C, that is six degree days above a 4°C reference point (time in days multiplied by difference in temperature from the reference point of 4°C).

TABLE 12.1. Degree days above and below intended temperature

Crop	Storage temperature		Oct	Nov	Dec	Jan	Feb	March	April	May	June
Sprouting	4°C	Above		101	68	53	51	96	142		
potatoes		Below		28	55	70	65	39	11		
Ware	7°C	Above	123	48	28	20	20	47	77	156	235
potatoes		Below	29	64	109	130	118	83	36	14	2
Crisping	10°C	Above	63	16	8	5	5	18	33	89	157
potatoes		Below	61	122	182	208	187	147	81	40	10

LEVELS OF INSULATION

The amount of insulation needed to avoid freezing can be calculated by using formulae developed by D. I. Bartlett of the Agricultural Development and Advisory Service (ADAS).

Frost Protection

If no heat is provided to a stored mass during cold weather the temperature will fall. If damage through freezing is to be avoided, the heat stored in the produce must be sufficient to maintain a heat flow through the structure without the minimum store temperature falling below 1°C.

Therefore where the heat in the stack cannot be redistributed any way but naturally (i.e. no recirculation system exists) the following formula should be used for calculating the R value of the walls:

$$R = 0.246 \, (T_i - T_0) - 0.193$$

where R = thermal resistance of the wall excluding surface resistance $(m^2 °C/W)$
T_i = minimum safe store temperature (°C)
T_0 = design outside temperature (°C).

Example 12.4

$T_i = 5°C$ (for short periods of time with process potatoes)
$T_0 = -3°C$
this gives R = 1.775.
Therefore including surface resistance $U = 0.56 \, W/m^2 °C$.

If the heat from the stack can be redistributed by recirculation the following formula should be used to calculate the 'U' value for the whole structure. (The ceiling is also important in this case as the heat can be redistributed).

$$U = \frac{0 \cdot 004628 \, Q_{cap} \left[- \log_n \frac{T_i - T_0}{T_s - T_0} \right]}{At}$$

U = design 'U' value (W/m^2°C)

Q_{cap} = mass of stored produce × specific heat (kJ) (recommended that calculations doen on 75 per cent capacity)

T_i = minimum safe store temperature (°C)

T_0 = average ambient temperature for the design period (°C)

T_s = normal storage temperature °C

A = area of walls and roof of store (m^2)

t = design period days

$\log_n$ = natural log obtained from tables.

Example 12.5

Table 12.2

	'U' value in W/m^2°C
Bulk ware store (long term)	0·75
(short term)	1·00
Bulk process store (long term)	0·55
(short term)	0·75
Box ware store (long term)	1·10
(short term)	1·14
Box process store (long term)	0·75
(short term)	1·00
Refrigerated ware bulk store	0·40
Refrigerated process bulk store	0·35
Refrigerated box ware store	0·50
Refrigerated box process store	0·40
Ambient ventilated potato sprouting store	0·75
Refrigerated potato sprouting store	0·50

Consider 500 tonne ware bulk store (19·2 × 13·7 m, 5 m to the eaves with a roof pitch of 22·5°).

$T_i = 2°C$

$T_0 = -2°C$

$T_s = 7°C$

$A = 656 \, m^2$

$t = 10$ days

$Q_{cap} = 500 \times 1,000 \times 3 \cdot 6 \times 0 \cdot 75 = 1 \cdot 35 \times 10^6$ (specific heat of potatoes 3·6 kJ/kg).

therefore $U = \dfrac{0.0046 \times 1.35 \times 10^6}{656 \times 10}\left[-\log\dfrac{(2--2)}{(7--2)}\right]$

$U = 0.947 \times 0.81$

$\quad = 0.77\ \text{W/m}^2\,^\circ\text{C}.$

Although the minimum insulation value that would be recommended will vary with situation and length of intended storage period, as typical values Table 12.2 may be helpful.

These figures are somewhat lower, that is of a higher standard than are often suggested, but with increasing cost of fuel, the emphasis on quality and the importance of cutting down waste, higher insulation values can be justified than in the past.

Economic Level of Insulation
When considering an economic level of insulation the following factors must be taken into account:
1. The cost of fuel used to heat or cool the structure and its efficiency of utilisation
2. The annual cost of the insulating material used
3. The annual cost of the capital plant
4. The loss in value of the produce stored as a result of moisture removed by the cooling system
5. The temperature being maintained within the structure
6. The period of operation and the ambient temperatures occurring during this period.

The equation developed by D. I. Bartlett for the general situation is rather complex.

$$R_{(min)} = \sqrt{\dfrac{86\cdot4\,(BH(1-s)/2{,}500) + HF + TP}{I}}$$

where $R_{(min)}$ = optimum thermal resistance $\text{m}^2\,^\circ\text{C/W}$

$\quad$ H $\quad$ = day degrees, $^\circ$C (above or below optimum temperatures)

$\quad$ s $\quad$ = sensible total heat ratio

$\quad$ B $\quad$ = product value p/kg

$\quad$ F $\quad$ = fuel cost p/kJ

$\quad$ T $\quad$ = maximum temperature difference $^\circ$C

$\quad$ P $\quad$ = annual cost of plant capacity p/W

$\quad$ I $\quad$ = annual cost of unit R value $\text{pm}^2\,^\circ\text{C/W}.$

The cost of unit R value is given by

$\quad$ I $\quad$ = KD

where K $\quad$ = k value of insulation W/m$^\circ$C

$\quad$ D $\quad$ = annual cost of installed insulation $\text{pm}^2\,^\circ\text{C/W}.$

This equation can be simplified in some situations. For example if the plant is already installed and only insulation needs to be specified

$$R_{(min)} = \sqrt{\frac{86\cdot4\,HF}{I}}$$

If, however, both the plant and the insulation need to be specified

$$R_{(min)} = \sqrt{\frac{86\cdot4\,HF + TP}{I}}$$

Example 12.6
Consider a ware potato store in the area near Cambridge, UK. The intended storage temperature is 7°C from November to March, electricity is 3·0 p/unit. An insulation material costing £80/m³ installed is used with k = 0·03 W/m°C.

H = 667 degree days (from Table 12.1)
F = $8\cdot3 \times 10^{-4}$ p/kJ
I = $80 \times 100 \times 0\cdot03 = 40$.
Therefore

$$R_{min} = \sqrt{\frac{86\cdot4 \times 677 \times 8\cdot3 \times 10^{-4} \text{m}^2\text{°C/W}}{40}}$$
$$= 1\cdot10\ \text{m}^2\text{°C/W}$$

Therefore taking into account surface resistance
U = $0\cdot80$ W/m²°C.

AVOIDANCE OF CONDENSATION

Condensation occurs on a surface when its temperature drops below the dewpoint of the air with which it is in contact. Therefore condensation occurs when relatively warm moist air meets a cold surface.

Condensation should be avoided in potato storage for three reasons:

1. The condensing surfaces remove moisture from the air which is largely replaced by moisture from the crop; therefore every litre of condensation is a direct loss of 1 kg of crop.

2. The loss of moisture by a crop can affect its appearance and therefore its marketability.

3. If condensation occurs on the ceiling water can drip back into the crop, making it more susceptible to disease development.

Normally in the long run the best method to prevent condensation forming is by the use of insulation on the walls and more especially the roof.

The level of insulation that is needed just to prevent condensation occurring on the surface can be calculated using the following equation.

$$R = \frac{(T_{dew} - T_0)}{9 \cdot 433 \, (T_s - T_{dew})}$$

R = thermal resistance $m^2 °C/W$
T_{dew} = dewpoint temperatures of the store air °C
T_0 = outside temperature °C
T_s = store temperature °C.

Table 12.3. Typical values for thermal resistance ($m^2°C/W$) to avoid condensation

Outside temperature °C	Inside conditions: relative humidity and temperature					
	4°C		7°C		10°C	
	96%	84%	96%	84%	96%	84%
10	—	—	—	—	—	—
5	—	—	0·25	0·02	0·78	0·11
0	0·42	0·02	1·13	0·19	1·66	0·32
−2·5	0·87	0·10	1·57	0·30	2·10	0·42
−5	1·31	0·17	2·01	0·40	2·54	0·53

Although the surface temperature and the store air temperature and humidity are the main factors in whether condensation occurs, the physical characteristics of the surface and the velocity of air movement across it also have an influence. Therefore if possible the walls and particularly the ceiling should be dark non-metallic and certainly not bright and polished. Also some air movement (e.g., recirculation) helps to cut down any possibility of condensation.

Although not directly on the subject of insulation, one method of reducing the possibility of condensation in a store where it is occurring is to warm the surface of the roof insulation. The idea is to avoid the surface temperature of the insulation dropping below the dewpoint of the store air. A heat source which will provide laminar flow of warm air up the roof slope is required. This can be done by electric fan heaters positioned at alternate ends of the building with perforated polythene ducting running the length of the building next to the ceiling at the eaves. The opening in the polythene duct should give the air direction up the roof slope. The heaters would be controlled by a thermostat positioned near to the roof surface set at about 2·5°C higher than the store temperature (the actual setting can be changed in the light of experience). The heater units should be wired in such a way that they are switched off when the main fan unit is in operation. The electricity consumption should not be excessive in most cases as the heaters will be on for only short periods.

SELECTION OF INSULATION MATERIAL

There is a wide range of insulation materials on the market all with slightly different characteristics. Therefore when choosing an insulation material a number of factors are listed below which should be considered:

Availability	self-explanatory
Insulation value	considered earlier in chapter
Type of material	foam, quilt, slab, composite panel (see below).
Cost of material .... *Cost of installation*	important to consider jointly (see below).
Structural strength	will strengthening members be required or will the insulation material be sufficient?
Effect of moisture	will a vapour barrier be needed and where? (see below).
Effect of vermin	can vermin attack it?
Air-tightness	is it easy to make a well sealed building? (considered earlier in chapter).
Fire requirements	it is always important to check fire regulations before installing insulation.
Vulnerability to damage ...	can the insulation be easily protected from damage or easily repaired?

Type of Material
Insulation materials come basically in four types; slabs, quilts, foam and composite panels.

Slabs normally require wooden battens for mounting as well as good fitting between the joints and a vapour barrier, although some closed cell polystyrenes have a built-in vapour barrier.

Expanded polystyrene slabs, for instance, have a high insulation value but as they are permeable to moisture they require a vapour barrier. Also as they are not structurally strong they require careful fixing or are liable to crumble.

Care is needed in the sealing between slabs to ensure there is no heat leakage and the tongue and groove type boards can help in this respect.

Metal fixings can cause a temperature bridge unless their heads are covered in bitumastic paint or buried in the insulation material (nylon nuts and bolts can be useful).

Vermin can attack slab insulation, in particular if the board is already damaged.

A clear face should be left, if at all possible, as this assists air flow and if there are no projections it is less likely to be damaged.

Examples of slab insulation material are expanded polystyrene sheets and extruded polystyrene sheets.

Quilts (*e.g.*, mineral wool) always need a good vapour barrier as they are very permeable to water and air. Moisture drastically affects the insulation properties (the insulation value of glass fibre can be reduced by around 30 per cent for an increase of 2 per cent in moisture). Quilts can very easily slip out of place if not carefully installed. One further problem with quilts is that as they are sandwiched between boards they cannot be seen and cases have been known where the quilt has been almost totally destroyed by moisture or vermin. Care should be taken that the quilt is not compressed at installation.

Foam sprayed on can be a costly form of insulation and never looks really tidy, but particularly when insulating an old building the overall cost of this material and its installation can be less than for other materials. It should always be carefully applied by an approved contractor with particular attention to ensure an even application of the required thickness. One advantage of spray-on insulation is that it does seal any cracks in the building. Care is required in some situations to ensure that no birds are able to attack the insulation. Examples are polyurethane foam or urea formaldehyde foam.

Composite panels come in a very wide variety of specifications, some with vapour barriers and some without, so care should be taken to ensure the right one is selected. Some include cladding materials so they can be used for outside walls. Although composite panels are quite expensive per square metre they can be quickly and cheaply installed. The totally sealed panels made by metal bonded to foamed or slab insulation, if properly made, are vapour

PLATE 12:1
Insulation sheets in a potato store

PLATE 12:2
Insulated panel store
being erected

Geerlofs Ltd

proof and take into account thermal expansion. There are composite panels which have structural strength and can be used for thrust walls.

An example of a composite panel could be aluminium foil, expanded polystyrene, polythene sheet vapour barrier, steel coating.

Cost of Material and Installation

As mentioned above the total cost of installation and material can be very different from the cost of the material alone. For instance glass-fibre may cost less then £1/m² for material but installation including vapour barriers, battens etc., could cost six times as much.

The cost of different grades of the same material can vary by a factor of two and also bulk buying versus small quantities can mean a difference of 40 per cent in price.

The cost of different materials therefore depends on what the insulation has to do and whether it needs protecting, the quantity required, the grade and also how cheaply it can be installed. One further point is that with most insulation materials there can be significant variations in cost between suppliers. A comparison of installed insulation materials is given in Appendix I, page 246.

Effect of Moisture

As mentioned previously moisture can seriously affect the insulation value of certain insulation materials such as glass-fibre. Therefore it is important to have some sort of barrier which will stop water being transmitted through a structure; this is called the vapour barrier.

The best type of vapour barrier is the metal sheet of a sealed panel but also adequate in order of efficiency are metal foil, polythene sheet or bitumastic paint.

The vapour barrier should be installed on the warm side but in many cases it is worth putting on both sides of the insulation as the vapour pressure of air is more dependent on temperature than relative humidity (in most cases a store at 96% RH will have a higher relative humidity than outside). For materials like glass-fibre, wood wool or straw panels it is strongly advised to encase it in a polythene envelope.

Great care should be taken to ensure that the vapour barrier is not damaged on installation and for this reason if a polythene sheet is being used it should be heavy gauge to cut down the risk of being torn.

SOLAR HEAT GAIN

As most potato storage is during the winter months the gain of heat to the structure by the sun can be considered negligible. When potatoes are being stored beyond the end of April with the assistance of refrigeration it can become a more important factor.

To cut down the solar heat gain a few simple precautions should be taken.

1. Choice of colour; a white surface will absorb 50 per cent of the radiation incident on it whereas a grey surface will absorb 85 per cent of the same radiation. It is worth remembering that asbestos sheeting 'weathers to a darker colour'.

2. Shading; diffuse sunlight has less radiation and so any way that the building or part of it can be shaded will cut down the solar heat again.

3. Thickness; the rate at which the solar radiation is transmitted depends not only on the insulation value of the walls and roof but also the thickness, and there may be time lag between the peak incident radiation and the maximum effect on the building. Therefore this 'flywheel' effect means that although the maximum radiation on a roof occurs at midday the effect may not be felt in the building until late afternoon. In some cases the building can be cooling off before the heat resulting from solar radiation ever gets through the structure.

4. Orientation; the best way to place a potato store is east–west with the long dimensions facing north–south. This is so that the rising and setting sun are shining against the shorter walls.

The method of calculating solar heat gain is complicated and has to be done for various times of day to find the worst case. Normally, provided care is taken in colour, shading, thickness and orientation, no difficulties occur. If it is necessary in a particular situation to calculate the solar heat gain the formula, graphs and tables can be found in The Chartered Institution of Building Surveyors' (CIBS) *Guide*.

SUMMARY

When considering insulation it is important to distinguish between thermal resistance R and thermal transmittance 'U'. When considering the insulation of a wall, roof or floor in total the 'U' value should be used as this includes surface resistance and in the rare cases where this applies, air movement in wall cavities.

Condensation can be eliminated or reduced by insulation although the physical characteristics of the surface and the velocity of air movement across it also have an influence.

The level of insulation required to just avoid condensation under design conditions can be calculated.

Localised heating within a building can be useful where particularly difficult condensation problems occur.

Selection of Insulation Material
The insulation value and cost of an insulation material are not the only factors to be considered; the others are: availability, type of material, cost of installation, structural strength, effect of moisture, effect of vermin, air tightness, fire requirements and vulnerability to damage.

References
BARTLETT, D. I., 'Occasional Note on Insulation for ADAS Mechanisation Advisory Officers' (unpublished).

LINDSAY, R. T., 'Insulation for Crop Storage Buildings', Farm Buildings Department National Institute of Agricultural Engineering. 'Fuel economy on the Arable Farm', Conference (1979) (unpublished).

The Chartered Institution of Building Surveyors, *Guide Book C*.

Appendices

APPENDIX I

Thermal Conductivity (k) of Some Materials

Material	$k(W/m°C)$
Aluminium	160
Asbestos sheet	0·23 to 0·40
Bitumen	0·16
Brick—common	0·81
Brick—engineering	1·20
Clay soil	1·50
Clay roof tiles	0·85
Concrete aerated	0·12 to 0·20
Concrete no fines	0·60 to 0·90
Concrete tiles	1·10
Concrete slabs	1·44 to 2·0
Copper	200
Cork granulated	0·04
Cork slab	0·05
Expanded polystyrene	0·037
Extruded polystyrene	0·029
Glass	1·05
Glass-fibre	0·036 to 0·04
Granite	2·50
Gravel	0·30
Hardboard	0·08
Limestone	1·50
Loam soil	1·20
Mineral wool felt	0·039
Mineral wool slab	0·045
Plasterboard	0·16
Plywood	0·14
Polyethylene	0·50
Polyurethane foam	0·026
PVC	0·16
Roofing felt	0·19
Sand cement	0·55

Material	$k(W/m°C)$
Sandstone	1·30
Sawdust	0·08
Steel	50
Straw bales	0·072
Straw slab	0·11
Timber soft wood	0·13
Timber hard wood	0·15
Urea formaldehyde foam	0·036
Vermiculite (loose)	0·065
Water (20°C)	0·60
Wood chipboard	0·150

(Increasing the moisture content, temperature or density of any material increases the k value)

Thermal Resistance of Air Spaces

Cavity 20 mm or more	0·18 $(m^2°C/W)$
Cavity 5 mm	0.11 $(m^2°C/W)$
Cavity one face clad with reflective foil facing into cavity	0·35 $(m^2°C/W)$

Surface Resistance

The surface resistance depends on the surface colour and air speed over the surface.

However, typical surface resistances (sum of inside and outside) are:

Roof $0·150m^2°C/W$
Walls $0·176m^2°C/W$.

Comparison of Installed Insulation Materials

Material	k $(W/m°C)$	Thickness (mm)	Vapour Barrier	Installed cost $(£/m^2)$	i $(£W/m^4k)$
Mineral wood fibres	0·045	75	yes	7·90*	4·74
Mineral wool mat	0·042	70	yes	7·30*	4·38
Glass fibre mat	0·040	75	yes	5·85*	3·12
Expanded polystyrene sheet	0·037	60	foil	3·40	2·10
Expanded polystyrene board	0·035	75	yes	8·10	3·78

Comparison of Installed Insulation Materials *(continued)*

Material	k $(W/m°C)$	Thickness (mm)	Vapour Barrier	Installed cost $(£/m^2)$	i $(£W/m^4k)$
Urea formaldehyde	0·033	75	yes	6·15	2·71
Cellulose fibres	0·032	75	yes	5·60*	3·58
Extruded polystyrene	0·029	50	no	5·50	3·19
Polyurethane sheet	0·023	35	foil	5·00	3·29
Polyurethane foam	0·023	42	no	5·00	2·74

* Includes asbestos lining and 0·15 mm polythene
(the index parameter *i* gives the cost of each material installed for a similar insulation value U = 0·5 W/m²°C).
Reference: C. Wathes, Agricultural Development and Advisory Service, Shardlow.

APPENDIX II

Estimated Long-term Average Degree-Days

Degree-days	Oct	Nov	Dec	Jan	Feb	Mar	Apr	May	Jun

Agroclimatic area 35 (103 m above sea level)
(Principally Somerset)

Degree-days	Oct	Nov	Dec	Jan	Feb	Mar	Apr	May	Jun
Above 3°C	245	125	92	80	79	105	171	257	339
Above 7°C	123	45	30	27	27	30	69	133	219
Above 10°C	53	12	6	5	4	4	22	52	129
Below 3°C	0	5	30	53	45	9	0	0	0
Below 7°C	2	45	92	123	107	58	18	0	0
Below 10°C	25	101	161	195	170	125	61	12	0

Agroclimatic area 16 (66 m above sea level)
(Principally Nottinghamshire)

Degree-days	Oct	Nov	Dec	Jan	Feb	Mar	Apr	May	Jun
Above 3°C	257	126	78	66	62	84	143	251	354
Above 7°C	133	43	22	19	18	25	54	128	234
Above 10°C	57	9	3	3	3	4	15	55	144
Below 3°C	0	3	38	66	59	34	2	0	0
Below 7°C	0	40	106	142	128	100	33	1	0
Below 10°C	17	96	180	219	198	171	84	21	0

Edinburgh (35 m above sea level)

Above 3°C	208	87	66	55	52	95	133	214	297
Above 7°C	90	17	14	12	11	33	45	92	177
Above 10°C	31	0	0	0	0	7	10	29	93
Below 3°C	0	6	38	65	49	30	1	0	0
Below 7°C	6	56	110	145	121	91	34	2	0
Below 10°C	40	129	189	226	195	159	88	32	6

Aberdeen (58 m above sea level)

Above 3°C	189	79	50	39	37	86	115	183	270
Above 7°C	73	15	6	3	3	28	35	67	150
Above 10°C	19	0	0	0	0	5	6	15	68
Below 3°C	0	10	41	60	48	39	4	0	0
Below 7°C	8	66	121	149	128	105	44	8	0
Below 10°C	47	141	208	239	209	176	105	50	8

Meteorological Office, Cambridge.
For the purpose of agricultural weather records, England and Wales are split up into 52 separate agroclimatic areas.

Accumulated Temperature (Degree-days)

Accumulated temperature can be defined as the integrated excess or deficiency of temperature to a fixed datum, usually called the base temperature, over an extended period of time.

Accumulated temperature is usually expressed in degree-days above or below a given base temperature.

Degree-days are the accumulation hour by hour of the number of degrees, above or below the desired base temperature, divided by twenty-four.

For example, if on a given day the temperature is above the base temperature for n hours and the mean temperature during that period exceeds the base temperature by m degrees the accumulated temperature above the base for the day is nm degree-hours or $nm/24$ degree-days. By summing the daily values arrived at in this way, weekly, monthly or yearly totals can be obtained.

In practice daily values of accumulated temperatures are often derived not from hourly values, but by a method involving the use of daily maximum and minimum temperatures. These are not only more practical for simple calculations but are often available when hourly temperatures are not.

Calculations of accumulated temperature based on daily maxima and minima have of necessity to assume some particular form of distribution of temperature throughout the day.

Daily totals of degree-days above 10°C and above 6°C, for some fifty-five locations throughout the UK, are issued by the Meteorological Office on the day following observation.

Reference: Meteorological Office Cambridge

APPENDIX III

Conversion Tables

Length

1 mm = 0·039 in	1 in = 25·400 mm
1,000 mm = 1 m	
1 m = 3·280 ft	1 ft = 0·305 m
1,000 m = 1 km	
1 km = 0·621 miles	1 mile = 1·609 km

Speed

1 m/s = 196·800 fpm	100 fpm = 0·508 m/s
1 m/s = 2·237 mph	1 mph = 0·447 m/s
1 km/h = 0·622 mph	1 mph = 1·609km/h

Area

1 m^2 (square metre) = 10·758 ft^2	1 ft^2 = 0·093 m^2
10,000 m^2 = 1 ha(hectare)	
1 ha = 2·471 acres	1 acre = 0·405 ha

Volume

1 l(litre) = 0·220 gal	1 gal = 4·545 l
1,000 l = 1 m^3(cubic metre)	
1 m^3 = 35·31 ft^3	1 ft^3 = 0·028 m^3

Mass (Weight)

1 g(gramme) = 0·035 oz	1 oz = 28·35 g
1,000 g = 1 kg	
1 kg = 2·204 lb	1 lb = 0·454 kg
1,000 kg = 1 tonne	
1 kg = 0·020 cwt	1 cwt = 50·802 kg
1 tonne = 0·984 ton	1 ton = 1·016 tonne

(Note error of 1·6% if 1 ton = 1 tonne is assumed)

Density

1 kg/m^3 = 0·062 lb/ft^3	1 lb/ft^3 = 16·019 kg/m^3
1 tonne/m^3 = 0·028 ton/ft^3	1 ton/ft^3 = 35·882 tonne/m^3

Volume Flow Rate

1 litre/s = 13·158 gal/min	1 gal/min = 0·076 litre/s
1 m^3/s = 2119 cfm	1,000 cfm = 0·472 m^3/s

(Note error of 6% if 2,000 cfm = 1 m^3/s assumed)

Ventilation Rate

0·02 m³/s/tonne = 40 cfm/ton

Power

1 Watt(W)	= 1 joule per second (J/s)		
1 kilowatt (kW)	=1·341 hp	1 hp	= 0·746 kW
1 kW	= 3,412 Btu/h	1,000 Btu/h	= 0·293 kW

Energy

1 joule (J) = 0·239 calories (cal)
1 cal   = 4·187 J
1,000 J   = 1 kilojoule (kJ)
1,000 kJ   = 1 megajoule (mJ)
1 kJ   = 0·948 Btu   1 Btu= 1·055 kJ

Pressure

$1 kN/m^2$ = 4·016 in water   1 in water gauge= 0·249 kN/m^2
                gauge
(kilonewton per square metre)
1 mm water gauge=0·039 in water   1 in water gauge= 25·4 mm water
                gauge   gauge
$1 kN/m^2$ = 1kiloPascal (kPa)
$1 kN/m^2$ = 0·145 psi   1 psi   = 6·895 kN/m^2
$1 kN/m^2$ = 0·010 bar
1000 m bar   = 1 bar
100 m bar   = 1·450 psi   1 psi   = 68·947 m bar

Application and Work Rates

100 litres/ha   = 9·091 gal/acre   10 gal/acre   = 110 litre/ha
100 kg/ha   = 75 units/acre   10 units/acre = 13·333 kg/ha
1 hectare/hour = 2·471 acre/hour   1 acre/h   = 0·405 ha/h
                (acre/h)
1 mm/ha/h   = 0·096 in/acre/h   1 in/acre/h   = 10·377 mm/ha/h
1 mm/ha/h   = 10 m³

Insulation

1 W/m²°C= 0·176 Btu/ft²°F   1 Btu/ft²°F   = 5·678 W/m²°C
         ('U' value)
1 W/m°C = 6·944 Btu in/ft²°F   1 Btu in/ft²°F= 0·144 W/m°C
         (k value)

Temperature

°C	°F
−10	14
− 9	16
− 8	18
− 7	19
− 6	21
− 5	23
− 4	25
− 3	27
− 2	28
− 1	30
0	32

$$°C = \frac{5}{9}(°F - 32)$$

$$°F = \frac{9}{5}(°C + 32)$$

- - - - - - - - - - - - -

°C	°F
1	34
2	36
3	37
4	39
5	41
6	43
7	45
8	46
9	48
10	50
11	52
12	54
13	55
14	57
15	59
16	61
17	63
18	64
19	66
20	68
25	77
30	86

INDEX